FROM THE
GROUND UP

Rethinking Industrial Agriculture

HELENA NORBERG-HODGE

PETER GOERING

JOHN PAGE

ZED BOOKS

in association with

THE INTERNATIONAL SOCIETY
FOR ECOLOGY AND CULTURE

From the Ground Up: Rethinking Industrial Agriculture (revised edition)
was published by Zed Books Ltd., 7 Cynthia Street, London N1 9JF, UK and
Room 400, 175 Fifth Avenue, New York, NY 10010, USA, and by the
International Society for Ecology and Culture (ISEC), a charitable
organisation based in Devon, England and Berkeley, USA, in 2001.

Distributed exclusively in the USA by Palgrave, a division of
St Martin's Press, LLC, 175 Fifth Avenue, New York 10010, USA.

Copyright © Helena Norberg-Hodge, Peter Goering
and John Page, 1993, 2001

First edition, 1993
Second (revised) edition, 2001

Cover designed by Helen Strang
Copyediting, production and design by
Denise Caignon, Steven Gorelick and John Page
Revised edition produced by Long House, Cumbria

Printed and bound in the United Kingdom
by Biddles Ltd., Guildford and King's Lynn

A catalogue record for this book is available from the British Library
US cataloging-in-publication data is available from the Library of Congress

ISBN   1 85649 993 6 Hb
ISBN   1 85649 994 4 Pb

FROM THE GROUND UP

Modern industrial agriculture is in crisis. In our obsession with 'efficiency' and short-term profit, we are losing all real connection with the natural world. As a result, the dream of global abundance promised by the introduction of chemical fertilisers, pesticides and hybrid seeds is becoming a nightmare of health risks, degraded land and ailing communities. The way we produce our food is destructive and quite simply unsustainable.

From the Ground Up: Rethinking Industrial Agriculture sets the decline of agriculture within the broader context of industrialisation as a whole, and explores some of the fundamental principles which underlie the 'growth-at-any-cost' thinking of modern society. At the same time, it documents the growing public distrust of conventional agricultural practices, and highlights some of the most promising alternatives leading to more sane, environmentally healthy ways of producing food.

This book is a valuable reference for those concerned with the future of agriculture – in the industrialised countries as well as in the South, where agricultural development continues to be modelled on the industrial ideal.

THE INTERNATIONAL SOCIETY FOR ECOLOGY AND CULTURE (ISEC) is a non-profit organisation based in Devon, England and Berkeley, California, USA. Its primary goal is to promote critical discussion of the foundations of modern industrial society, while at the same time examining the principles necessary for the emergence of more sustainable and equitable patterns of living.

ISEC is the umbrella organisation of the Ladakh Project, which for fifteen years has been undertaking a wide-ranging programme in the Himalayan region of Ladakh aimed at exploring alternatives to conventional development.

Foxhole, Dartington, Devon TQ9 6EB, UK
PO Box 9475, Berkeley, CA 94709, USA

HELENA NORBERG-HODGE is Director of both the Ladakh Project and ISEC. She was educated in Germany, Austria, England, France and the United States, as well as her native Sweden. Her formal training was in linguistics, including work at MIT with Noam Chomsky. She has lectured extensively on environmental issues in both Europe and North America, and is the author of *Ancient Futures: Learning from Ladakh* (1991), which explores the root causes behind today's environmental and social malaise. In 1986, she received the Right Livelihood Award, commonly known as the 'Alternative Nobel Prize'.

PETER GOERING graduated in Civil Engineering from Princeton University. He received his MA from the Energy and Resources Group of the University of California at Berkeley, a department which conducts interdisciplinary research into the relationship between resources, society and the environment. He is currently preparing his doctoral dissertation on 'Sustainable Development and the Contradictions of Modernism', while also working as ISEC's Research Coordinator.

JOHN PAGE was trained as a barrister in London. For the last decade he has coordinated the technical, educational and agricultural activities of the Ladakh Project, and is now Programmes Director of ISEC. He is the producer/director of two recent films: *The Future of Progress*, a compilation of interviews with internationally known environmentalists, and *Ancient Futures: Lessons from Little Tibet*, a documentary based on Ms Norberg-Hodge's book.

Contents

Appendixes

Acknowledgements

The authors would like to thank David Edwards, Todd Merrifield and Steven Gorelick for help with research, editing and production. Inger Källander (Alternative Farmers Association, Sweden) and Debra Van Dusen (Agroecology Department, University of California, Santa Cruz) read through various drafts.

We also benefited from the assistance of numerous other individuals who offered constructive criticisms of early drafts and pointed out fruitful lines of enquiry. These include: Miguel Altieri, Maria José Guazzelli, Phil Leveen, the staff of *The Ecologist*, Henry Osmaston, Arnold Schultz, the staff of the Soil Association, Christian and Renate Storm and Martijn van Beek.

We would also like to thank Denise Caignon for production and layout. Further editorial services were provided by Karen Kho, Camille Antinori and Kari Norborg Carter.

Preface

The logic of industrial development is to systematically pull people away from the land. In the North* only 2 or 3 per cent of the population is left in agriculture, and even that tiny number is declining year by year. Meanwhile, development in the South relentlessly pushes farmers into urban slums.

Not surprisingly, then, the voice of the farmer is very weak, and agriculture is rarely the subject of public debate. Even within the environmental movement, agricultural issues generally receive little attention, while at the level of international politics, they are typically seen as 'stumbling blocks' to progress on other, more important issues.

The authors believe the impact of capital- and energy-intensive agriculture—on the environment, on the economy, on the very fabric of society—demands that the whole subject be taken much more seriously. And if the damage which industrial agriculture has already caused is not sufficiently compelling, then the threat posed by biotechnology surely is. Agriculture is now in the process of changing the very nature of life. The questions which such manipulations involve are far too serious to be decided by a few 'experts' behind closed doors.

While aimed at concerned readers in every part of the world, the pages which follow focus primarily on agriculture in the North. This, after all, is where the process of industrialisation is most advanced. Moreover, it is the Northern model which is now being imposed on and emulated by the people of the South.

---

* Throughout this volume the term 'North' refers to the modern industrialised countries of North America, Europe, Japan, Australia and New Zealand. 'South' refers to the less industrialised nations sometimes referred to as the Third World.

A healthy farm culture can be based only upon familiarity and can grow only among a people soundly established upon the land; it nourishes and safeguards a human intelligence of the earth that no amount of technology can satisfactorily replace. The growth of such a culture was once a strong possibility in the farm communities of this country. We now have only the sad remnants of those communities. If we allow another generation to pass without doing what is necessary to enhance and embolden the possibility now perishing with them, we will lose it altogether. And then we will not only invoke calamity— we will deserve it.

Wendell Berry
The Unsettling of America

From Global to Local:
Sowing the Seeds of Community

Seattle – a Watershed?

Flying out to join the non-governmental organisations protesting in Seattle in November 1999, I was amazed to find that *The Economist* had devoted its cover story to the growing popular resistance to the World Trade Organisation (WTO) Millennium Round negotiations and to globalisation in general. We critics, the magazine claimed, were 'winning the battle for public opinion', with 'protectionist sentiments growing rapidly around the world.' As committed proponents of the 'free' trade dogma, *The Economist* was clearly alarmed that public dissent might increase the likelihood of a political stalemate that would prevent further deregulation and so 'fatally undermine the WTO'.[1] For campaigners used to working on shoestring budgets against the overwhelming might of corporate and government interests, this was heady stuff indeed.

As a founder of the International Forum on Globalisation (IFG), I was due to speak at an IFG conference held in Seattle's symphony hall, with seating for 2,500 people. We had worried that we might not attract anything like that number. At the event, not only was the hall packed – by a wildly enthusiastic audience applauding, it seemed, every word from speakers such as Vandana Shiva, Martin Khor, myself, and many others – but some 2,000 people had to be turned away. By all accounts, what Americans call ticket 'scalping' was rife outside, with $10 dollar tickets selling for $40. This was no rock concert nor heavyweight prize-fight; this was a teach-in on trade! As the Chairman of the US Federal Reserve Bank warned the global economic community: 'Beware the rumbling out there!'

But what does this rumbling signify? According to some politicians and commentators, it is merely the sound of a confused public stumbling through arguments about free trade and the global economy, and reacting 'emotionally' against endeavours such as the genetic modification of food. This sort of thing should be left to the 'experts', they insist; it is just too complex for 'ordinary people' to understand.

Complex it is; nevertheless, the great majority of protesters knew perfectly well why they were so incensed. Their criticisms were generally articulate and intelligent. When I was asked to speak on a Seattle radio show, a farmer – the head of a rural crisis centre in Kansas – turned to me and said authoritatively, 'You know, it's the free trade treaties that are killing us.' People around the world are rapidly waking up to the fact that the promise of jobs and universal prosperity through global trade is a hollow one.

Time and again, people had told me that it would be impossible to get anyone interested in big, complicated issues like trade policy, or in long words like 'globalisation'. Well, now it's happening, as part of an extraordinary alliance of environmentalists, human rights activists and people concerned with economic insecurity and the loss of their jobs, in both North and South. This has never happened before to anything like this extent, and I believe it is irresistible. The feeling at Seattle, above all else, was that resistance to the corporate-led global economy is a process that cannot be stopped.

One of the major pathways to a more critical stance on globalisation – feeding the anger that drove protesters onto the streets of Seattle – has been the increasing concern about the genetic manipulation of food. Much of the enthusiasm seen in Seattle was engendered by the strong stance that consumers have taken against genetically modified organisms (GMOs), particularly in Europe, and by the victories that they won in the previous couple of years. In the original edition of this book, we warned of the coming marriage of biotechnology and unregulated global trade. This cornerstone of globalisation is attracting ever more attention, as movements opposed to both 'Frankenfoods' and 'free' trade continue to grow, and as people become aware of the intimate links between the two. Around the world, an increasing number of people see this unholy marriage as constituting a severe threat to food security, the environment and human health. Both biotechnology and 'free' trade are integral components of the global industrial food system, which is not only leading to a fundamental reorganisation of how our food is produced and marketed, but is also creating lifeless rural areas and overcrowded, energy-intensive cities, while at the same time severing our direct relationship with the natural world.

The Global Industrial Food System

Over several hundred years, thousands of diverse, locally adapted agricultural systems around the world have been replaced by a single, industrial food system. Among the indicators of this shift are a dramatic reduction in the number of farmers and a concomitant expansion in the size of farms, a huge increase in the size and scope of agricultural markets, a startling decrease in agricultural biodiversity and a tightening control by transnational corporations over the world's food supply.

The negative effects of industrial agriculture are clearly spelled out in the pages of this book. For several decades now, there has been much research into the effects of pesticide residues on soil and agricultural ecosystems, and upon human health. Increased awareness of these problems has helped to spawn a fast-growing demand for organic foods, and has stimulated research into alternative agricultural methods, including traditional systems of agriculture. Much less articulated, however, is the devastating effects of lengthening the distance between producer and consumer – effects that are not addressed simply by avoiding the use of pesticides and other chemicals.

Foremost among these effects is a huge increase in the transport of food, and its attendant ecological costs. It is no longer in doubt that greenhouse gases are altering the global climate – making weather everywhere not simply warmer, but more unstable, unpredictable and extreme. The stakes are so high that to continue 'business as usual' seems irrational at best, especially when it means encouraging people everywhere to consume food transported thousands of miles, instead of food produced next door. It is a notion that borders on lunacy. Yet this is exactly what government policies in almost every country promote, and as a consequence, food miles within the industrial food system have risen astronomically in the last half-century. A typical plate of food in the United States today has accumulated some 1,500 miles from source to table.[2] On average, each item of food now travels 50 per cent further than it did in 1979.[3]

There is little merit to the argument that all this food transport simply enables people to consume fruit, vegetables and other foods unavailable from nearby sources. In 1996, for instance, Britain exported 47 million kilogrammes of butter, while *importing* an almost identical amount, 49 million kg. The situation is almost as bad for milk: of the 173 million litres of milk Britain imported, a large portion was unnecessary, since 111 million litres were also exported.[4] Figures are similar for other commodities, and for other countries. For the most part, this excessive transport

benefite's of mass transportation

benefits only a few large-scale agribusinesses and speculators, which take advantage of government subsidies, exchange-rate swings and price differentials to shift foods from country to country in search of the highest profits. Although proponents of 'free' trade argue that fleets of cargo ships, trucks and planes carrying the same commodities in opposite directions somehow leads to economic efficiency, the current system is, by any reasonable measure, absurdly *inefficient*. As economist Herman Daly has pointed out: 'Americans import Danish sugar cookies, and Danes import American sugar cookies. Exchanging recipes would surely be more efficient.'[5]

Foods grown locally have other energy-related advantages over industrial foods produced hundreds or thousands of kilometres away. Since local foods are more often consumed fresh, they usually require less packaging, processing and refrigeration: a frozen carton of peas, for example, requires 2.5 times as much energy as fresh peas, while an aluminium can of peas uses 4.5 times as much.[6] Furthermore, there is the problem of what to do with the waste that results from all the packaging required by industrial foods. In the UK, at least a quarter of household waste is packaging, two-thirds of which is from food.[7] More and more land must be devoted to burying this huge amount of waste, because it is produced on a scale that natural processes cannot possibly absorb. Much of the packaging is non-biodegradable plastic, and even paper cannot break down in dense, poorly aerated landfills.[8] Burning all this refuse is an even worse option: trash incinerators contaminate the air with hundreds of pollutants, including carcinogenic substances such as dioxin, while leaving behind an ash contaminated with heavy metals and other toxins.[9]

Growing for faraway markets is also eroding the nutritional quality of our food. Fruit and vegetable varieties are bred with characteristics to suit the global marketing system, and nutritional content is not one of them. For industrial foods, hardiness under monocultural growing conditions and the ability to transport and handle well are valued more highly than nutritional content. And because the vitamins in almost any food are gradually lost from the time of harvest, even 'fresh' foods from the industrial system are less nutritious if they have been harvested days or even weeks before reaching the kitchen table. Tomatoes, for example, are often picked green and hard so that they can survive mechanical harvesting and long-distance transport, and then ripened in rooms pumped full of ethylene gas, which artificially initiates ripening. These tomatoes are much less tasty and nutritious than the ripe tomato from the local farm or back garden, plucked from the vine and eaten the same day.

 food quality

Another high priority is visual 'perfection'. Decades of agribusiness and supermarket advertising – combined with numerous senseless regulations – have persuaded people that fruits and vegetables must conform to narrow standards of size, shape and colour. Customers expect to find only bright red, unmarred apples, potatoes that are 'properly' shaped and without blemish, and carrots that are adequately large, straight and orange. Most western consumers are now so disconnected from agricultural reality that heirloom varieties of unusual shape or colour are widely unrecognised and not considered to be real foods at all. And food grown in living soil where insects are allowed to survive – sometimes leaving their mark on the produce – is considered substandard, even though it is likely to be better tasting and more nutritious than its more 'perfect-looking' industrial cousin.

The global industrial food system is as damaging for farmers as it is for consumers. One of the most conspicuous features of the system is the shrinking percentage of the price of food that farmers receive. In part, this is because a large number of corporate intermediaries – international traders, food processors, distributors and supermarkets – are taking an ever bigger cut. In the United States, the real price of a market basket of food has increased about 3 per cent since 1984, while the farm value of that food has *fallen* by more than 35 per cent.[10] Today, only 21 cents of every dollar spent on domestically produced food in the US goes to farmers, the remaining 79 cents going to middlemen and marketers.[11] With that 21 cents, farmers have to pay for inputs, farm labour, machinery, rent, and so on. Many are lucky to break even after a season of hard work.

Farmers are being economically squeezed in other ways as well. 'Free' trade policies force farmers to compete with others around the world, often in places with more favourable labour costs or climate. What is more, the market for an export-oriented farmer's production can suddenly evaporate owing to currency fluctuations or a recession thousands of miles away. In the Third World, farmers are being persuaded to commodify their production, growing for the market rather than for themselves and their own communities. This ties them to the same unstable global market forces. The pressure to commodify leads to monocultural production, which also leads to greater instability. As part of this process, family members (usually men) are pressured to sell their labour in the money economy, and frequently leave the farm to seek work in the city. The consequent loss of labour on the farm creates problems for the family members (usually women and children) who remain behind. Eventually, many farming families are forced off the land altogether, leaving their ancestral homes and rural communities for the anonymity of the big city. Here they will almost certainly exist on the economic margins, living in one of the Third World's ever-expanding urban slums.

In both the Third World and the West, much industrial agricultural work is done by hired labourers, often immigrants, who have very little power or control over their working conditions. They typically perform monotonous labour, for poor wages, and are often exposed to harmful chemicals, being forced to handle produce that is covered with pesticide residues. Their living conditions are often abysmal. If they are not given (typically substandard) housing by their employer, they must seek out similar housing in town. In addition to these harsh living and working conditions, they are often treated with little respect by other social groups. Rural peoples are often seen as 'backward' and stupid. If they are immigrants, they may face even harsher persecution. Economic hardship can bring a backlash against these 'outsiders', who have left their own countries only because economic circumstances forced them to.

The non-farming members of rural communities lose out as well. As farms consolidate and rural people leave for the city, the local businesses that supported the farm community see their customer base shrink. As small town high-streets become more and more drained of life, large chain retailers, such as Wal-Mart, set up shop to serve the remaining population. These large retailers serve a much wider catchment area, making it necessary for rural people to travel further to satisfy their basic shopping needs, and contributing significantly to the pressures on small, local businesses. Evidence of this trend has been the rapid decline of specialist grocers, butchers, bakers and fishmongers, with a total loss of some 6,000 shops in the UK between 1990 and 1995.[12] Family-run grocery shops now account for only 12 per cent of the UK vegetable market, whilst the supermarket share has grown from 8 per cent in 1969 to 72 per cent in 1995.[13]

Destroying Diversity

The consequences of the global food system for the real diversity of available foods have been brutal and rapid. Each *quartier* of Paris in the 1970s had its own colourful market, selling wonderful fruits, all kinds of vegetables, meats, superb cheeses and wine. This diversity originated at no great distance, most of it coming from different regions of France, if not from the immediate surroundings of Paris. Today it can be difficult to find garlic in Paris that has not travelled from China. In the supermarkets, Chilean grapes and Californian wines are increasingly commonplace. The diversity of

French foods is in decline, and they are becoming ever more expensive.

Similarly, in the villages of southern Andalusia in the 1980s, almost all the food sold came from the villages themselves or the immediate region: goat's cheese, olives and olive oil, grapes, fresh and dried figs, wine and many different kinds of meat. Today you will find hardly anything on sale that originated in the village. Olives may come from the surrounding region, but they will have been sent to the metropolis to be packaged in plastic and then returned. Virtually everything sold is vacuum-sealed in layers of plastic. Even cheese rinds are now made of plastic.

It might be argued that, the issue of unnecessary transport aside, an increase in trade invariably leads to increased choice for consumers. After all, are not consumers now exposed to all kinds of new and exotic foods in their supermarket, foods that cannot be produced locally? While in a sense this is true, the reality is that the purported diversity offered by the global economy and its supermarkets is based on modes of production that are condemning producers to monoculture. The perceived expansion of choice obscures a startling loss in real diversity. Whereas a few decades ago, one could find more than a dozen varieties of apple or tomato in the local market, today there are typically just three or four. These are the same three or four varieties that you would find in a supermarket on the other side of the country, or on another continent – the few select varieties that have the characteristics that are most conducive to the demands of long-distance transport. As part of this process the diverse cheeses from France, the apple varieties of Devon and the olive groves of Andalusia are progressively being replaced by standardised hybrids, to suit the long distance, large-scale marketplace. Examples of the once-famed range of more than 200 regional English apples are now a rarity in English shopping baskets – an example of what 'choice' actually means in the global economy.

This lack of real diversity at the market is mirrored in an increasing number of the world's agricultural fields. The consequence of more and more farmers orienting their production towards far-away markets has been a startling loss in agricultural biodiversity. In China, of the 10,000 wheat varieties in use in 1949, only 1,000 remained in the 1970s. In the US, 95 per cent of the cabbage, 91 per cent of the field maize, 94 per cent of the pea, and 81 per cent of the tomato varieties have been lost. According to the UN Food and Agriculture Organisation (FAO), approximately 75 per cent of the world's agricultural diversity has been lost in the last century.[14] The implications of this trend for food security are ominous. Not only are there fewer kinds of foods being raised and eaten around the world, but diversity within the few remaining staples is being lost as well. Since a field planted in monoculture is more susceptible to devastation by pests and blight, the risks rise exponentially when much of the entire planet's arable land is planted in virtually identical strains. In 1970, for example, 80 per cent of the corn planted in the US shared a common genetic heritage. When a maize blight struck, it quickly destroyed more than 10 million acres of corn.[15]

Globalisation and the Dogma of 'Free' Trade

The global industrial food system arose within the context of the corporate-led global economy. Employing taxpayers' money, and at the behest of big business, governments have funded the motorways, high-speed rail links, tunnels, bridges and communications satellites that make it possible to sell foods from the other side of the world at a lower price than local produce. Taxpayers also subsidise the aviation fuel and energy production on which this long-distance trade depends. The continual expansion of these infrastructures, along with the increased global trade that results, leads to the breakdown of local and regional economies, as they become tied to one global system. Since the 1940s, international trade has come to dominate a growing number of national economies. In this period, world trade has grown twelve-fold. Imports and exports now make up a much larger proportion of economic activity than ever before, with international trade amounting to some US$5.5 trillion annually.[16] This explosive increase in global trade has fed the growth of the trading bodies – transnational corporations (TNCs) – many of which have more economic clout than entire nations. In fact, a comparison of national GDPs (Gross Domestic Products) with the annual revenues of TNCs shows that half of the 100 largest economies in the world are now corporations.[17]

The outline of today's globalised economy was established at the 1944 Bretton Woods conference, where western leaders met to design a new financial architecture for the post-war period, in order to keep the growth economy alive and prevent another depression. This was to be accomplished by drawing more of the world's economies into the orbit of the consumer economy, thereby dramatically expanding the market for industrial goods while assuring unfettered access to the planet's natural resources. With this end in mind, three supranational institutions were established: the World Bank, the International Monetary Fund (IMF) and the General Agreement on Tariffs and Trade (GATT).

In the Bretton Woods scheme, the World Bank would provide funding for major 'development' projects, including huge centralised energy plants, long-distance transport networks, and high-speed communications systems, thereby creating the physical infrastructure required by huge trading corporations. The IMF would work to impose a standardised economic architecture – with Western-style consumer growth as the foundation – on every national economy. Strict 'structural adjustment' policies would be imposed on borrowing countries that did not adhere to that plan. GATT, meanwhile, would serve to increase every nation's dependence on long-distance trade by keeping tariffs low, removing other perceived 'barriers to trade', and turning ever more realms of life into globally tradeable commodities.

For the South, this framework ushered in the era of 'development', with goals and policies that followed seamlessly from the colonial era that preceded it. Though ostensibly more noble in its aims, the results of this framework were strikingly similar: a Northern economic model, based on industrial production, trade and economic growth, was to be systematically imposed throughout the Third World. As in the colonial period, a large portion of the South's production and resources would continue to flow Northward.

In 1994, member nations of GATT created a new and powerful governing body, the World Trade Organisation (WTO), to set trade rules and settle disputes. Member countries which join the WTO implicitly agree to reorganise their national economies in ways that are more conducive to foreign trade and investment.[18] This reorganisation includes the privatisation of industry and the dismantling of any social programme, or labour, environmental or health regulation that could be interpreted as a 'non-tariff' barrier to trade. In this context, practically any law or regulation that a government may have adopted in order to protect its environment or its citizens – such as laws regulating the harvesting of tuna to ensure that dolphins are not killed in the process, or laws forbidding the sale of manufactured goods that were produced using child labour – may be perceived as GATT-illegal, with the offending country forced either to repeal the offensive law or to pay huge fines to the country that brings the complaint.

At Seattle in 1999, trade ministers were meeting to negotiate rules for a new 'Millennium Round', which would further eliminate hindrances to the speculative flow of capital and trade around the globe, and would place greater limitations on any government's ability to protect its citizens and environment.

Part of the Seattle agenda was to develop further the 'Agreement on Agriculture', bringing the production of food more firmly into the global trade arena – thereby under the control of TNCs – and forcing governments to remove tariffs and subsidies designed to support domestic producers and maintain the integrity of their countries' rural areas. Also on the current trade agenda are Patents on Life and Trade-Related Aspects Of Intellectual Property (TRIPs). Under current rules, biotech TNCs can essentially develop and patent marketable products in the lab, using genetic material and centuries-old traditional knowledge from anywhere on the planet, without giving compensation to the people or communities from which the knowledge or genetic material was obtained.

Both of these issues are of crucial importance to Third World countries, in which a majority of the population still lives on the land, and where most of this valuable genetic material and traditional knowledge resides. For Third World governments, the first priority is food: they assert the right of every country to guarantee the production of food for its own people and the right to support its own farmers. They insist that countries should have the democratic right to establish their own national economic development policies, including agriculture policy. Most are also strongly opposed to the patenting of life forms, and support the conservation of their own countries' plant genetic resources. Within the current WTO framework for negotiations, the most economically powerful countries exert the most influence; most Third World delegates are essentially bullied into signing agreements against their countries' interests – in which they had no hand in writing. In Seattle, however, these delegates demanded to be heard. Emboldened by 'the rumbling out there', they jointly declared that they would not agree to any new agenda for a new round of WTO talks. Collapse of the talks thereby became a certainty.

The current orthodoxy is that the liberalisation of trade, through the reduction of tariff and non-tariff barriers, increases competition and efficiency, releases more productive resources for growth, and generally leads to a higher 'standard of living' for all people. But all over the world, in both North and South, this trend towards 'liberalisation' is eroding laws that are designed to protect citizens and the environment, vastly enhancing the ability of TNCs to roam the planet freely in search of places where labour, environmental and health standards are weakest, and where they can extract the most surplus for the lowest cost. Governments, whose economies are increasingly linked to unstable market forces, have become beholden to these businesses, providing them with huge financial incentives to set up shop in their neighbourhood, and developing the infrastructures necessary for global trade (all at taxpayers' expense). In this process, governments have become increasingly less answerable to the needs and desires of their citizenry. Furthermore, economic 'liberalisation', along with huge government expenditures on trade infrastructures and other subsidies for big business, has created an economic playing field on which small-scale, local producers cannot possibly compete. This has led to the loss of livelihood for millions upon millions of small farmers, fishermen, producers and shop-owners. Rising GDPs, large corporate profits and booming stock markets obscure the declining quality of life for a majority of the world's people.

Genetically Engineered Food

A major new tool in the service of the global industrial food system is biotechnology. GMOs came to widespread public attention for the first time in 1996, when the media began to carry stories of how soybeans grown in the US were genetically engineered by Monsanto to be resistant to their best-selling herbicide 'Round-up'. Over 40 per cent of the US soybean harvest is exported, often mixed with conventional soybeans. The American Soybean Association rejected calls to keep the genetically modified soya separate on the basis that it was 'substantially equivalent' to ordinary soya.[19] The theory of 'substantial equivalence' has been at the heart of international guidelines and testing of GMOs. According to this principle, selected chemical characteristics are compared between a GMO and any non-modified variety within the same species. If the two are closely similar, the GMO does not need to be rigorously tested, on the assumption that it is no more dangerous than the non-modified equivalent. (Conveniently for biotech corporations, while a GMO is deemed to be 'substantially equivalent' to its non-modified cousin when it comes to testing and regulation, it is somehow deemed to be substantially *different* when it comes to patenting rights).

Unfortunately, 'substantial equivalence' is flawed as a basis for risk assessment. GMOs may contain unanticipated new molecules that could be toxic. In 1989, 37 people died in the United States after consuming a food supplement called L-tryptophan that had been produced from genetically engineered bacteria. It was regarded as 'substantially equivalent' and passed as safe for human consumption.[20] A variety of enzymes produced from genetically engineered micro-organisms is used throughout the food industry. None of these foods has been subject to the kind of long-term safety studies applied to new drugs.

The idea of 'substantial equivalence' grows out of the argument that, because people have been inter-breeding plants and animals for many thousands of years, genetic engineering is simply an extension of traditional practices, rather than a radical new method that requires extreme caution and its own strict rules. However, an elementary understanding of what genetic engineering entails makes it clear that these claims are absurd. In traditional forms of breeding, variety is achieved by selecting from genetic traits already existing within a species' gene pool. Breeders can cross varieties, or even species, that wouldn't necessarily reproduce if left to themselves, but nature imposes strict limits to this practice. A rose can cross with a different kind of rose, but not with a mammal. A horse can reproduce with a donkey, but not with a caterpillar. Even when different species that are closely related succeed in reproducing (such as a horse and a donkey), the offspring (such as a mule) are usually infertile, thereby prohibiting the newly created organism from reproducing itself. These natural reproductive boundaries are essential to the integrity of any species.

In contrast to traditional breeding, genetic engineering involves identifying the genes that code for a specific trait or characteristic in a species, and transferring those genes into another species, often across entire taxonomic phyla or kingdoms. For example, a gene or sequence of genes in a species of arctic fish (such as flounder) that leads to the production of a chemical with antifreeze properties can be spliced into the genetic material of a tomato or strawberry, in order to make it frost-resistant. It is now possible for scientists to introduce genes taken from bacteria, viruses, insects, animals or even humans, into plants. This new technology manipulates organisms in a fundamentally different and hazardous new way, precisely because it allows us to transcend the reproductive limitations imposed by nature, and because its anticipated effects can never be completely certain.

Genetically engineered foods already on the market in the US include corn, soybeans, potatoes, squash, tomatoes, chicory and papaya, as well as milk and other dairy products from cows treated with a genetically engineered growth hormone (rBST). BST (also known as rBGH – recombinant bovine growth hormone), is a genetically engineered hormone injected into one-third of dairy cows in the US to increase milk production. It is currently banned in Europe. There is a real possibility that the US Government and Monsanto, the manufacturer of BST, will use the WTO to force the product into the EU. The BST hormone causes a five-fold increase in the protein IGF-1, which passes into the milk. An EU Scientific Committee report links IGF-1 to breast and prostate cancer. It causes increased infection and disease in cows, making them produce more pus, and causing a substantial increase in mastitis, sores, foot problems, and reproductive disorders. These problems in turn increase the use of antibiotics, which of course end up in the milk.[21]

There is growing evidence that genetic engineering poses new risks to ecosystems, with the potential to threaten biodiversity, wildlife and truly sustainable forms of agriculture.[22] Critics of the technology argue that once GMOs have been released into the environment, they may transfer their characteristics to other organisms in a way that is uncontainable. A study by the National Pollen Research Unit shows that the wind can carry viable maize pollen hundreds of kilometres in 24 hours.[23] Current trial plots where genetically modified crops are grown have a 'buffer zone' of only 200 metres between them and non-modified crops of the same species. Genetically modified crops can cross-pollinate with other crops and wild relatives, and pass on their resistance to weedkillers or viruses. The offspring may become persistent weeds within arable fields. Ever more chemicals will be needed to control the problem.[24]

Since the original publication of this book, many of the concerns of biotechnology critics have been proven justified, both inside and outside the laboratory. For example, one study showed that ladybirds feeding upon aphids that had eaten genetically modified potatoes lived half as long and laid 38 per cent fewer eggs, which were four times more likely to be unfertilised and three times less likely to hatch.[25] Another study, at Cornell University in the US, revealed that monarch butterfly larvae feeding upon milkweed that had been sprinkled with genetically modified corn pollen were significantly impaired in their development, with a large increase in premature death.[26] In several countries where genetically modified crops are grown, farmers who do *not* use modified seed have reported contamination by pollen from nearby modified crops, with their own crops eventually exhibiting the GMO characteristics.

The food biotech industry is dominated by a handful of multinational corporations holding interests in food, additives, pharmaceuticals, chemicals and seeds. These corporations are beginning to monopolise the global market for GMOs. This process is being facilitated through the WTO, which makes it difficult for countries to refuse a new product or technology, even if they have concerns about its potential impact on health or the environment. Patenting rights allow corporations to patent new genetically engineered varieties. This gives them control over huge areas of the market. The high cost of researching, developing and patenting new crops means that larger companies are likely to continue to dominate the market. This process is also being assisted by a planned programme of acquisitions and mergers, incorporating seed companies, genetic engineering companies and other related interests. Monsanto, for example, spent $8 billion on new acquisitions between 1996 and 1998. According to Robert T. Fraley, co-president of Monsanto's agricultural sector, 'This is not just a consolidation of seed companies; it's really a consolidation of the entire food chain.'[27]

Part of the current trade agenda is the forging of an agreement on trade in GMOs. At issue is the right of governments in Europe and elsewhere to respond to the wishes of the general populace and ban or restrict the importation of genetically modified food. The US government, at the behest of agribusinesses, grain traders and seed corporations, have fought rigorously against any such restrictions, arguing that there is no proven scientific basis for doubting the safety of these food products, and therefore, no WTO-legal basis for restricting their importation. Leaving aside the claims of 'no proven scientific basis', it is disturbing that in this process, democracy seems to have been thrown out of the negotiations altogether – that the will of a large majority of citizens does not seem to matter.

A Shift in Consciousness: Resistance ...

In response to the worrying developments described above, citizen groups around the world are beginning to realise that it is the corporate-dominated global economic system that is the prime culprit behind many of today's social and environmental problems. Increasingly, activists and citizen groups of all types are joining together and pressing for major policy changes at both national and international levels, in order to take control of the global financial markets that are systematically subordinating human and environmental well being to a volatile, speculative market.

A very visible example of growing activism has been the aforementioned massive public resistance in many European countries against the genetic modification of foods. In the face of biotech multinationals and the US government trying to force genetically modified foods down the throats of European consumers, public pressure to restrict or even ban imports of these foods has been escalating. As a consequence, it has become impossible for European governments to ignore their voters. In the name of sovereignty and consumers' rights, some of these governments even seem willing to risk a trade war with the US, and the breakdown of WTO talks in Seattle was at least partly due to differences on this issue. In addition, the four major supermarket chains in Britain, and several others on the

European continent, have publicly stated that they will not allow genetically modified ingredients to be used in their own brands. The US-based snack food giant, *Frito-Lay*, recently announced that it would not use genetically modified corn in its snack chips. In Montreal, in January 2000, agreement was reached on the Cartegena Protocol on Biosafety, establishing an international regulatory regime based on the 'precautionary principle' to manage the unique risks of the handling, transfer and use of genetically modified organisms. This means that if there is any doubt as to the absolute safety of a GMO, governments should take the precaution of keeping it off the market, rather than forcing it on to the market until proven unsafe. Although the Montreal agreement unfortunately does not provide for any means of enforcement, this acceptance of the 'precautionary principle' is a clear moral victory for activists and consumers, and it works against corporate agricultural and biotech interests, who argue that restrictions should not be imposed, unless justified by 'sound science'. All of these positive developments were the result of citizen groups and individual consumers making their opinions known.

A previous, and less publicised, victory for citizens was the stalling of the Multilateral Agreement on Investment. The MAI was an international agreement, written mainly by representatives of transnational banks and corporations and government trade officials, which aimed to force governments to relinquish much of their power, especially their ability to protect their citizens and maintain social, environmental and health standards. A relatively small number of activists and informed citizens put pressure on governments around the world and forced the stalling of the agreement – a feat made even more impressive by the fact that these negotiations were conducted in secrecy. Most elected officials, even ministers, were unaware of the existence of the MAI!

A third example is the US Department of Agriculture's retreat from its plans in 1998 to weaken organic standards, in order to allow large agribusinesses to take advantage of the increasingly lucrative market for organically grown foods. The new guidelines would have even allowed for the inclusion of irradiated, genetically modified, and toxic-sludge-treated foods under the 'organic' label. After the USDA offices were flooded with thousands of irate letters from consumers, the department backed away from its plans. The USDA has recently issued a new set of proposed organic guidelines, which generally reflects the values of organic food advocates and incorporates most of the consumers' wishes. However, big business still threatens to water down and distort organic standards.

There is much citizen resistance taking place in the South. In India, where action against the global economy is snowballing, a 'Declaration of the Indian People Against the WTO' has recently been drawn up by a group of farmers, academics, NGOs, unions and others. It attacks the 'WTO–IMF–World Bank trinity', which 'has the potential not only to suck the sweat and blood of the masses of two-thirds of the world, but has started destroying our natural habitats and our cultural diversity'.

Also in India, the ten-million-strong Karnataka state farmers association (KRRS) has been involved in destroying Kentucky Fried Chicken outlets, occupying the offices of the giant seed company Cargill and, most recently, burning Monsanto's genetically modified crops, all in the wider context of protesting about the effects of globalisation on the subcontinent. The KRRS has also organised an 'Intercontinental Caravan' of Indian farmers and others, to tour the world, raising awareness about the problems of globalisation.

But undoubtedly the most encouraging and significant expression of resistance was the mass protest in Seattle. As mentioned earlier, the demonstrations there involved an extraordinary array of farmers, business people, mothers with young children, environmentalists, indigenous people and members of labour unions. Protesters numbered in the tens of thousands, and brought world-wide attention to a process that has over the years taken place in total secrecy. The message of the people marching in the streets was very clear: globalisation is not a natural or evolutionary process; it is about specific trade agreements and government policies, and these must be changed. The atmosphere of resistance created by these protests undoubtedly played a major role in the collapse of these talks, and they have certainly ensured that future trade decisions – which so fundamentally affect the well-being of the planet and its citizens – will no longer be made outside the glare of public scrutiny.

These successes truly signal a dramatic change in public awareness. The *Economist* article discussed above noted that 'the critics are not just against the WTO, they are against globalisation broadly defined'. Ordinary people are becoming aware that 'governments are supporting corporations to the detriment of jobs and the environment'.[28] As a result, the warning to business and governments is clear: 'Globalisation is not irreversible'.[29] The whole dogma of 'free' trade has been based on the notion that deregulation increases freedom (to trade). Increasingly apparent, however, is the reality that 'deregulation' actually involves the imposition of rules friendly to big business, in place of the hard-won environmental and human rights protections instituted by national governments under pressure from the public. Never before has there been such public resistance and awareness when free trade treaties have been negotiated. For the first time, there is real hope that the madness of economic globalisation can be brought to a halt.

... And Renewal: the Local Food Movement

Alongside this widespread, and increasingly effective, resistance to the corporate-led global economy, a plethora of positive micro-trends at the grassroots level is demonstrating the alternative to globalisation: localisation. Probably the strongest and most significant aspect of this trend is the local food movement. It is now overwhelmingly clear that globalisation is destroying local food production. As described above, in this process food security is threatened, the nutritional quality of food is eroded, pollution increases, and biodiversity, rural landscapes and regional distinctiveness in diet are homogenised. The genetic engineering of new food varieties threatens to take us further down this destructive path. In response to these developments, the local food movement – local production for local consumption – has become one of the most successful grassroots examples of economic localisation in action.

Local Food Production

The benefits of local food production are many. Growing for local markets makes small-scale organic agriculture much more viable, and the diversity encouraged by local marketing obviates the need for toxic chemicals and other off-farm inputs. Crops are less susceptible to blight because diversified farms are more resilient. If disease does strike, it will affect only a relatively small portion of the farm's total output. Pests are less of a problem because the agricultural environment encourages the presence of natural predators. Weeds are less of a hindrance because intercropping – growing different crops in the same space – naturally helps to suppress them, and there is less space between crops for them to flourish. What weeds there are can either be mechanically suppressed by hand pulling or fire, or simply tolerated. (Many so-called 'weeds' have valuable uses in their own right, and the term 'weed' is usually used to refer to any plant that interferes with the growth of monocultures for the market, irrespective of that plant's usefulness as a source of food or medicine). The decreased dependence upon inputs dramatically reduces the environmental impact of food production. Non-renewable natural resources are conserved, with farmers instead using the resources that abound on the farm itself, many of which are considered 'wastes' in industrial food production systems, and soils and watercourses are not poisoned. The smaller scale obviates the need for large, expensive farm machinery, and thereby allows the incorporation of trees and hedges into the agricultural landscape, providing a valuable habitat for birds and animals, and improving the aesthetic quality of the rural environment.

Contrary to common belief, small-scale, diversified food production is also better at meeting people's needs. The orthodox view of agricultural development holds that industrial agriculture – with its consolidation of land, mechanisation and use of chemicals – has vastly increased agricultural productivity. In fact, however, the productivity of industrial agriculture is largely a myth, propagated for years by the beneficiaries of this type of agriculture. Study after study, carried out in diverse locations all over the world, shows that small-scale, diversified agricultural systems almost always have a higher *total* output per unit of land than large-scale monocultures.[30]

Local Food Marketing

Faced with a wasteful and increasingly hazardous food culture, people are beginning to appreciate the advantages of local food, and are working to rejuvenate markets to obtain it. A variety of proven local marketing methods are currently being tailored to suit the needs of different communities:

Farmers' Markets

Farmers' markets were once common throughout the world, but experienced a major decline when large-scale monocultural production made local marketing economically unviable. Now, however, there is a resurgence of these markets. In the UK, the first farmers' market in recent years, in the city of Bath, generated much public interest, leading to a wave of new markets throughout the country. Since the early 1990s, the UK went from having no farmers' markets at all, to having over 140.[31] Farmers' markets are growing rapidly in North America as well. The US Department of Agriculture's directory listed 2,675 farmers' markets in 1998, over 50 per cent more than there were just four years earlier.[32]

Farmers' markets are sometimes held in a permanent structure, but more often occupy a section of street closed off to traffic. Most of the producers selling at these markets are small-scale, and even if they are not certified organic, they tend to use fewer pesticides than large-scale monocultures. Consumers have a range of in-season fresh produce to choose from, often harvested that same day. At most markets, they can also choose from a variety of other products, such as honey, fresh jams and preserves, ciders and juices, bread, cut flowers and potted plants. Many have vendors selling a variety of meats and dairy products, most of which are free of the hormones and antibiotics found in goods that come from large livestock enterprises. Some farmers' markets even feature live music, played by either paid performers or street musicians. All of these markets promote a sense of community, both through the friendly, relaxed shopping environment they create, and through the fact that money spent there supports local enterprises, and remains within the community.

Community Supported Agriculture (CSAs)

CSAs are the next best thing to growing your own food. The basic model is simple: members pay producers for a certain number of weekly deliveries in advance, and every week, the boxes of produce are delivered, either to the subscribers' homes, or to a central pick-up point. The benefits are obvious: consumers help small-scale, local farmers by providing a guaranteed market for their produce, and, in return, growers provide a weekly share of fresh food for a relatively low price. Most offer a mix of eight to twelve vegetables, fruits and herbs per week; some link up with other CSAs to maintain diversity; and others offer value-added products such as cheese, honey and bread. As they are growing for actual people, rather than for an abstract market, farmers want to provide a reasonable variety of produce, which thereby gives them an incentive to diversify their production, which in turn encourages them to employ more ecological practices.

CSAs not only enable consumers to establish a personal relationship with the person who grows their food, they also provide an opportunity for urban consumers to reconnect with the land. With most CSAs, the farmer welcomes visits from subscribers, perhaps even organising 'workdays' that enable subscribers occasionally to help out on the farm. Most important, consumers have the benefit of being able to eat produce that is much fresher and more nutritious than nearly anything they could buy at the supermarket. Members know where their food originates and how it was produced, and farmers receive payment in advance, rather than when the harvest is in. In this way, trust and mutual support is restored to the vital relationship between farmers and consumers.

There are currently some 600 CSA operations in the USA, involving 100,000 consumers, and a turnover of $10–20 million per year.[33] In the UK, there are now nearly 200 produce box schemes, selling to more than 45,000 households, and representing sales of £22 million.[34] A local food-promoting scheme in the Forest of Dean, begun in the late 1990s, sold nearly £325,000-worth of local food to local people in its first year. The 'Forest Food Directory' lists 32 different food producers, with products ranging from organic and free-range meat, through to vege-box schemes and local cheeses.[35]

A recent study of 83 CSAs in the USA, carried out by Timothy Laird and reported by Richard Douthwaite, has shown what people most value from them. More than 60 per cent of the farmers said that the most successful aspect of their operations was the strengthened bonds between people, resulting in networks that: 'reconnected people with the land and reconnected farmers with the people who eat the food that they grow'. Only about one-third of farmers mentioned the value of financial stability.[36]

People buying food direct from the producers are often very enthusiastic about the quality, and about the manner in which it is bought. In her book *Local Harvest*, Kate de Selincourt quotes a satisfied vege-box customer: 'My husband says it's like having Christmas every week. The quality is superb, it's sort of a lucky bag ... the kids rush to see what we've got. There is no possible comparison with the taste. You feel really sorry for people going to the supermarket.'[37]

Farmers are also satisfied with such direct relationships: when farmers are allowed to sell in the local marketplace, more of the profit stays in their hands. Currently, when the consumer buys food for £1 in the supermarket, the farmer very often receives less than 5 pence. The consumer spends 95 pence of that pound on transport, packaging, irradiation, colouring, advertising and corporate profit margins. But when these links are closed, the farmer receives more money and the consumer pays less. Both win. Kate de Selincourt asked farmer Pat Finn why she sells direct to customers rather than through a supermarket or butcher's shop: 'We can't provide what they call "portion control": everything the same size every time... We really enjoy the personal side of the work – it is nice to think that we have become so friendly with people just through business.'[38]

The joy of a direct connection between producers and consumers is often that their ideals coincide. They want the same things: human-scaled and human-paced production with high quality. They both want freshness, variety and a fair price. Both social life and business often flourish when suppliers and consumers form face-to-face relationships.

The Promise of Local Food

These local food systems are not an idealistic dream: they are a reality, now, and they are showing that they can be replicated across the world. They do not need to grow bigger: the farmer does not need to produce more and more to flourish, does not need to sell at ever greater distances. These systems are proliferating everywhere. They are taking the economy from global to local, and proving that it can be done.

But for such local food systems genuinely to flourish and multiply, changes at policy level are clearly necessary. The current trade and finance policies described earlier are artificially lowering the prices of industrially produced foods by shifting the costs of production on to the community, forcing citizens to pay for the global trade infrastructures and subsidies to big business that industrial food requires. If groups campaigning for sustainable farming, wildlife issues and better food do not take these hidden subsidies into account, and do not challenge the economic basis of our current monocultural, export-based food system, they risk falling into the trap of arguing that consumers should pay more for better food – when, as farmers markets show, they can actually pay less. The industrial approach marginalises the poor, who often cannot afford healthy, high-quality food. Furthermore, to overlook hidden subsidies is to miss a fantastic opportunity: if these resources were diverted towards decent agriculture and retailing, society would produce better food at no extra cost at all.

Recognising the consequences of current economic policies also gives agricultural and environmental groups common cause with those campaigning for social justice and human rights internationally. As clearly demonstrated by the experience of Seattle, these diverse bodies are now beginning to join hands to demand a different set of policies, and the redrawing of the global economic map.

The most important thing to remember is that we do have the power to change things. The destructive global economy can exist only as long as we are prepared to accept and subsidise it. We can reject it. And we can start by enjoying the wealth of benefits from re-linking farmers and consumers. Fresh, local food for all may be one of the most strategic – and certainly the most delicious – ways to reverse economic globalisation.

Notes

1. *The Economist*, vol. 353, no. 8147, 27 November 1999.
2. Debi Barker and Jerry Mander, *Invisible Government: The World Trade Organization: Global Government for the New Millennium?*, San Francisco: International Forum on Globalization, 1999, p. 22.
3. Department of Environment statistics, cited in H. Raven and T. Lang. *Off Our Trolleys? Food Retailing and the Hypermarket Economy*, London: IPPR, 1995.
4. Ministry of Agriculture, Fisheries and Food, *Agriculture in the United Kingdom, 1997*, London: MAFF, 1998. According to SUSTAIN, in 1997, the UK imported 126 million litres of liquid milk, while exporting 270 million litres;

imported 23,000 tonnes of milk powder, while exporting 153,000 tonnes, 135,000 tonnes of which went outside the EU. In that year, the UK also imported 115,000 tonnes of butter, 51,000 tonnes of which was from outside the EU, and exported 67,000 tonnes of butter, 27,000 of which was exported outside the EU. In 1996, the UK imported 434,000 tonnes of apples, 202,000 tonnes of which came from outside the EU. Over 60 per cent of UK apple orchards have been lost since 1970. In 1997, the UK imported 105,000 tonnes of pears, 72,000 tonnes of which were from outside the EU. 'Food Miles – Still on the Road to Ruin? An assessment of the debate over the unnecessary transport of food, five years on from the food miles report', Sustain – the alliance for better food and farming, October 1999.

5. Herman Daly, 'The Perils of Free Trade', *Scientific American*, vol. 269, no. 5, November 1993, p. 51.

6. J. Koojiman, 'Environmental assessment of packaging: sense and sensibility', *Environmental management*, vol. 17 no. 5, New York: Springer-Verlag, 1993; SAFE Alliance, *Food miles report*, London: SAFE Alliance, 1996.

7. Anon., 'Do you need all that packaging?', *Which?*, London: Consumers' Association, November 1993, p. 5.

8. Non-biodegradable packaging is not the only waste that goes into landfills, and we are now squandering a valuable resource in our failure to utilise organic waste. A quarter of London's waste (900,000 tonnes per year) is green and putrescible, much of it from food (T. Garnett, *Growing Food in Cities: a report to highlight and promote the benefits of urban agriculture in the UK*, London: SAFE Alliance and National Food Alliance, 1996). For millennia, this organic waste has been an important resource for farmers, either as compost or as food for livestock. Now it is a liability, which must be trucked away and dumped into dense landfills.

9. Environmental Research Foundation, 'Incineration News', *Rachel's Environment & Health Weekly*, no. 592, 2 April 1998.

10. Robert C. Taylor, Professor of Agriculture and Public Policy at Auburn University, in testimony before the US Senate Agriculture Committee hearings on concentration in agribusiness, January 1999. Cited in A. V. Krebs, *The Agribusiness Examiner*, no. 57, 23 November 1999.

11. Krebs, op. cit.

12. Retailing Enquiry, Mintel, March 1996.

13. D. Hughes, 'Dancing with an elephant: building partnerships with multiples', paper presented at The Guild of Food Writers' conference, 'The Vegetable Challenge', London, 21 May 1996.

14. From an FAO study, based on 150 country reports, *State of the World's Plant Genetic Resources*, Rome: FAO, 1996.

15. Jack Doyle, *Altered Harvest*, New York: Viking, 1985; FAO statistics, www.fao.org.

16. IMF Statistics Department, *International Financial Statistics*, February 1999, vol. 53, no. 2, Washington, D.C.: International Monetary Fund, 1999.

17. Hoover's Inc., *Hoover's Handbook of World Business, 1997*, Austin, Tex:

Hoover's Business Press, 1997; *The World Economic Factbook*, 4th ed., London: Euromonitor, 1996.
18. C. LeQuesne, *Reforming the World Trade Organisation. The Social and Environmental Priorities*, Oxford: Oxfam, 1996.
19. American Soybean Association, 'European Response to Genetically Modified Soybeans', November 1996.
20. Luke Anderson, 'Genetically Engineered Food, No.5', Greenpeace, www.greenpeace.co.uk
21. Ibid.
22. See R. Steinbrecher and Mae-Wan Ho, 'Fatal Flaws in Food Safety Assessment: Critique of The Joint FAO/WHO Biotechnology and Food Safety Report', 1996, www.psagef.org/fao96.htm
23. Science and Technology Select Committee Hearing, 26 April 1999, quoted in Greenpeace UK and Soil Association, 'The True Cost of Food', London: Greenpeace UK, June 1999.
24. Greenpeace UK and Soil Association, op. cit.
25. Science and Technology Select Committee Hearing, 26 April 1999, op. cit.
26. John E. Losey, Linda S. Rayor and Maureen E. Carter, 'Transgenic pollen harms monarch larvae', *Nature*, vol. 399 no. 6733, 20 May 1999, p. 214.
27. Quoted in J. Flint, 'Agricultural industry giants moving towards genetic monopolism', Telepolis, Heise Online, 1998.
28. *The Economist*, op. cit.
29. Ibid.
30. Peter Rosset, 'The Multiple Functions and Benefits of Small Farm Agriculture in the Context of Global Trade Negotiations', *Policy Brief* No. 4. Oakland, Calif.: Institute for Food and Development Policy, September 1999; R. Albert Berry, and William R. Cline, *Agrarian Structure and Productivity in Developing Countries*, Baltimore: Johns Hopkins University Press, 1979; Gershon Feder, 'The Relationship between Farm Size and Farm Productivity', *Journal of Development Economics*, vol. 18, 1985, pp. 297–313.
31. Soil Association (UK), Local Food Links campaigner, personal correspondence.
32. United States Department of Agriculture, National Directory of Farmers Markets, Washington, D.C.: USDA, Agricultural Marketing Service, November 1998.
33. This assumes an average share of $550, an average number of members of 50, and 600 CSAs.
34. Soil Association, *The Organic Food and Farming Report, 1999*, Bristol, UK: Soil Association, 1999, p. 25.
35. M. Dunwell and K. de Selincourt, *Forest Food Directory: A Guide to Local Food Production in the Forest of Dean*, Cheltenham, UK: Vision 21, 1997.
36. T. Laird (1995), reported in Richard Douthwaite, *Short Circuit: Strengthening Local Economies for Security in an Unstable World*. Totnes, UK: Green Books, 1996.
37. Kate de Selincourt, *Local Harvest*, London: Lawrence & Wishart, 1997, p. 164.
38. Ibid., p. 167.

Industrial Agriculture: Broken Promises

The Context of Industrial Agriculture

M odern agriculture is widely thought to be one of the great achievements of the industrial age. Since the Second World War, crop yields per acre have escalated, and efficiency—as measured by yield per unit of human labour—has increased exponentially. The numbers—at least some of them—look quite impressive.

The complete picture, however, is very different. Around the world, in fact, agriculture is in grave crisis. In the name of growth, modern methods of farming have degraded the environment, threatened human health, and impoverished rural communities. The way we produce our food is destructive and quite simply unsustainable.

Where did we go wrong? And how might we change our ways, so as to move towards a more viable relationship with the earth?

To find answers to these questions, we need to look not only at specific agricultural policies and practices, but at the broader political, economic and cultural context from which industrial agriculture has emerged. In turn, this requires a wide-ranging review of some of the fundamental principles underlying industrial society as a whole.

One of the key tenets of industrial culture is that human beings are separate from nature, and that we can manipulate and control the natural world to serve our needs. According to this view, the world can be understood by objectively examining it piece by piece, as one might examine a machine. Nature can be reduced to separate and static 'building blocks', which can be studied in isolation and then rearranged to our best advantage.

This reductionist perspective has allowed the earth under our feet to be seen as little more than a 'factor of production', soil as more or less inert matter, ecosystems as 'resources' to be exploited. In mainstream circles today, the notion of a 'living earth' receives lip service at best; the thrust of modern society is based on the de-animation of the world around us.

This narrow scientific world view goes hand in hand with an equally narrow economic paradigm. Modern economics is concerned almost exclusively with factors that can be reduced to numbers. GNP, the principle yardstick now used to measure national wealth, is based solely on the exchange of money. Non-monetary transactions—whether within the household in industrialised economies or within subsistence economies in the South—are ignored. So too are all other non-quantifiable factors, such as sustainability, social cohesion, psychological well-being and aesthetics.

The narrow focus on economic growth allows a whole range of problems to be accepted as part of the 'price of progress'. The breakdown of family life, individual alienation, spiritual poverty, and the destruction of community are all seen as mere 'side effects' of the unquestioned push to increase GNP.

By the same token, it is assumed that the environment has an unlimited capacity to supply resources and absorb wastes. In pursuit of immediate material benefit, the long-term health of the environment and the interests of future generations are largely ignored.

Science and economics have become the driving force of cultural change, and together have served to define some of the basic characteristics of modern industrial culture. They have devalued all but the most highly specialised knowledge; they have given rise to ever greater standardisation, in terms not only of production but even of cultures; and they have brought about increased economic, political and demographic centralisation. The impact of these fundamental trends on agriculture has been enormous.

Specialisation: A Narrow View

Today's agricultural scientists work in subdisciplines focused on extremely specialised fields of knowledge. Members of each discipline tend to confine themselves to their own narrow area of study, and give relatively little consideration to how their work fits into the broader picture, or to the long-term impact of its application. Research into the design of new pesticides, for example, will typically be focused almost exclusively on the 'target' pest. Such questions as the impact of the pesticide on other, potentially beneficial insects, or the effect on human health of chemical residues in food or drinking water, will often be all but ignored. Similarly, scientists who devise a new technology to improve agricultural productivity may be unaware of its impact on the incomes of small farmers.

Specialisation extends to the farmers themselves. In order to take advantage of new technologies, farmers are under tremendous economic pressure to concentrate on a single area of production. Once committed in this way, they are much more vulnerable to fluctuations in markets, whether in the form of rising input costs or falling product prices. Moreover, they are often unable to return to more diversified practices because they have invested so heavily in specialised equipment or in the expansion of their farms. Those farmers whose crops remain diversified receive almost no technical, financial, or educational support from a system dedicated to specialised farming.

Standardisation: The Drive to Homogenise

A primary goal of modern science is to find universal laws which would allow human beings to better control and manipulate nature. In its pursuit of such laws, science distorts the real world, by simplifying and standardising the objects of study. As a result, the findings of science are often invalid when conditions deviate from the assumed standard. Increasing nitrogen, for instance, enhances plant growth only if a myriad of micronutrients remains available, while hybrids will outperform traditional varieties only when soil, climate, and chemical inputs are optimised.

Standardisation is a critical factor in the modern drive towards economic efficiency. Standardised inputs have allowed manufacturers to supply standardised products to mass markets of homogenised tastes. Farmers throughout the industrialised world now follow the same pattern. They use the same seeds, the same chemicals and the same machines. Plants are bred for uniform development and ripening, for ease of harvesting and transportation, and in accordance with the cosmetic standards of large supermarket chains. Meanwhile, thousands of regionally-adapted species and varieties have been driven to extinction because they have failed in some way to meet the narrow requirements of the industrial food production system.

Agricultural practices no longer reflect the rich diversity of nature, but conform to supposedly universal standards acceptable to

5

governments and corporations. So little attention is paid to the diversity of the natural world that, for example, standards developed in temperate climates are often transferred unmodified to the tropics.

Far from promoting efficiency, as is commonly supposed, standardisation is a very *inefficient* way of farming. Rather than bringing forth the full potential of each individual piece of land and micro-climate, industrial agriculture reduces all land to the lowest common denominator, and exploits each field in essentially the same way.

Centralisation: Disempowering the Small Farmer

Each step of the agricultural process, from the education of farmers to the processing and packaging of produce, is today determined by ever more centralised government and corporate interests. Ever larger transportation and marketing networks are disempowering the individual farmer. The latest round of GATT (General Agreement on Tariffs and Trade) threatens to extend these networks still further, concentrating power over the whole global market in fewer and fewer hands.

Farmers are increasingly dependent on decisions made off the farm. As a result, the health of local ecosystems and rural communities is declining, while the number of small family farms is shrinking year by year. The process is a remorseless one. In its pursuit of 'economies of scale', the industrial system continues to exacerbate the cycles of decline.

Narrow scientific and economic ways of looking at the world have become deeply embedded in the way we think about agriculture, often blinding us to the serious problems we face. Even when the problems are recognised, the 'solutions' put forward generally represent 'more of the same,' and thus only serve to make matters worse. Meanwhile, attempts to rekindle traditional patterns of nurturance and stewardship are dismissed as 'uneconomic', romantic and woolly-headed.

New Seeds:
Meeting Corporate Needs

O ne of the central features of industrial agriculture is the use of hybridised seeds. Until recently, there was a tremendous range of seeds around the world, each one reflecting the soil and climate of the particular region in which it was found. Now, however, diversity is being eradicated—with potentially devastating results.

The new varieties were bred to respond to inputs of fertilisers, pesticides and water; under perfect conditions, they can produce substantially higher yields than traditional seeds. Experience has shown, however, that yields are often much lower than those of traditional varieties when industrial inputs—especially nitrogen—are denied.[1]

In general, new varieties are not well-adapted to climates that are sub-optimal. Moreover, later generations of hybrid seeds lose the 'vigour' of the original cross, with the effect that farmers have to buy new seed every year. Often the seed itself needs to be re-engineered in order to remain ahead of pests and disease.

The rapid adoption of these new seeds has caused a precipitous decline in the number of plant species under cultivation. As more and more farmers plant high-yielding varieties, the pool of genetic resources gets smaller. As a consequence, the whole agricultural base is weakened. In a monoculture, disease or pests can destroy vast areas of cropland at a stroke and bring economic ruin. In 1970, a maize blight in the United States destroyed fifteen percent of the crop. Fully eighty percent of the maize planted that year shared a common genetic heritage, and was thus potentially at risk.[2]

Ironically, plant scientists depend upon traditional seeds in order to develop new disease-resistant strains. However, efforts to save seeds in seed banks have proved largely ineffective. There is a growing realisation that the only effective way to maintain genetic diversity is by continuing to cultivate a large number of varieties.

In the industrialised countries, plants are often bred specifically to improve aesthetics, to facilitate harvesting and processing or to increase their resistance to pests. As a result, their taste and nutritional value are sacrificed. An increasing number of the tomatoes grown in the United States, for example, are square, hard and relatively tasteless. Their only real virtues are that they are easy to pick with machines and can be transported long distances for distribution and processing. Similarly, much of the large, flawless fruit that fills supermarket shelves these days is watery and insipid.

Agriculture & Biodiversity

Industrial agriculture contributes significantly to one of the foremost environmental problems of today: the loss of biological diversity. Genetically uniform crops are now replacing the diverse varieties farmers planted traditionally. Wild plants and animals have also suffered. One recent study determined that in Germany 513 plant species are endangered or extinct as a result of agriculture, making agriculture the leading contributor to the decline in biodiversity in the country. [3]

The mechanisation of farming has led to the removal of hedgerows and vegetation along field borders. Such areas are critical for the survival of a wide range of plant and animal species, especially during the months when fields are bare. [4]

Industrial agriculture's push for greater output has led farmers to convert natural meadows into chemically-dependent pasture monocultures. Ninety-seven percent of Britain's meadows—along with their rich and varied flora and fauna—have been destroyed in the last forty years. [5]

Birds and mammals that feed on soil invertebrates (particularly earthworms) have been hard hit: the sterilisation of the soil that results from the use of chemical fertilisers and pesticides has robbed them of their food supply. For example, an English study found a close correlation between badger populations and the abundance of earthworms. [6] A multi-year Danish study that tracked bird populations found that twenty-four species of birds, all important farmland species, were more abundant on organic farms than on land farmed industrially. Eleven of these twenty-four species had declined since 1976. [7] Agricultural chemicals kill wild plants and animals and upset food chains off the farm as well, by drifting or leaching into terrestrial or aquatic wildlife habitat.

Seed resources are increasingly concentrated in the hands of corporations from the rich parts of the world, a trend which will no doubt continue as new varieties are developed through genetic engineering. On the other hand, most of the germ plasm—the raw materials for the development of new seeds—comes from the poorer countries, where traditional varieties can still be found in relative abundance. The conflict over the control of these resources—which has already begun—is likely to worsen in the years to come. Already, giant corporations in the industrialised countries, including Shell, ICI, Ciba Geigy, ITT and Unilever, are buying out smaller seed companies and rushing to patent new varieties. Often these corporations engineer seeds requiring chemical inputs which they also manufacture; the chemical giants Dupont, Ciba Geigy, and Bayer are leaders in this trend. In other words, seeds are being sold to the highest bidder, rather than being produced in the interests of the small farmer or the consumer.[8]

Chemical Fertilisers: Artificial Abundance

A rtificial fertilisers are an integral part of Western farming systems. Over the last few decades, they have combined with other industrial inputs to significantly improve yields around the world. The widespread use of synthetic fertilisers, however, has given rise to a number of increasingly severe problems. It has further exposed farmers to the pressures of inflation, contributed to the degradation of agricultural ecosystems, and threatened both environmental and human health.

Since the production of one kilogram of nitrogen fertiliser requires the energy equivalent of about one-and-a-half litres of oil, fertiliser prices are closely linked to the cost of fossil fuels (Figure 3-1). Between 1970 and 1980, world oil prices rose from around two dollars to over thirty dollars per barrel. The cost of fertiliser rose proportionately. For a variety of reasons, however, prices paid to farmers did not rise to the same extent, and many farmers saw their incomes severely squeezed. Especially hard hit were farmers in poorer countries, where scarce foreign exchange had to be used to purchase petroleum and fertilisers, generally from foreign multinationals. The huge bill for farm inputs was a significant factor in many countries' spiralling debts. Although energy prices fell during the 80s, events in the Middle East caused prices to fluctuate wildly during 1990 and 1991, underlining the volatility of world energy markets. Dwindling reserves coupled with continued geopolitical insecurity make it likely that prices will rise still further in the future.

The great majority of the phosphorous that farmers apply is mined from deposits that have built up over centuries. Since the rate of phosphorous removal greatly exceeds the formation of new deposits, the phosphorous fertiliser on which industrial farmers depend is, in effect, a non renewable resource. While reserves are fairly large, they are concentrated in relatively few places in the world. With demand growing, it is only a matter of time before existing supplies become inadequate.

Figure 3-1. Index of fertiliser prices paid by farmers in the U.K. compared with index of crude oil prices

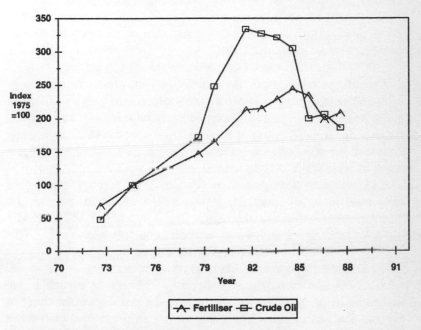

Source: FAO Fertiliser Yearbook, 1980, 1990. (Food and Agriculture Organisation, Rome); *Annual Energy Review*, 1991 (U.S. Energy Information Administration, Washington, D.C.)

Environmental Effects

When synthetic fertilisers are first introduced, yields increase appreciably. However, as the natural fertility of the soil is degraded, the higher yields become more difficult to sustain. The 1984 World Development Report of the World Bank concluded that there is 'evidence that sustained use of chemical fertilisers can decrease soil fertility.'[1]

11

Most farmers apply only nitrogen, potassium, and phosphorus (N, K, P) to their land, while plants also need at least 14 different minerals. Minerals such as zinc, iron, copper, manganese and magnesium, which are critical to plant growth, are often not replaced. The lower organic content of soils associated with the use of inorganic fertilisers can sometimes result in decreased availability of micronutrients in the soil. Farmers able to afford them have started adding expensive supplements. However, providing micronutrients through fertilisers has proved very difficult. Proper dosages are hard to assess, and imbalances can lead to deficiencies in other micronutrients and the build-up of minerals to toxic levels.

The widespread use of synthetic fertilisers has allowed farmers to abandon practices—such as crop rotation and the incorporation of plant and animal wastes into the soil—which had previously maintained soil fertility. The availability of artificial fertilisers has also led to the continuous cropping of monocultures. As a result, the organic content of the soil declines, leading to compaction and general degradation of soil structure.

Compaction slows growth by decreasing the soil's ability to hold water, and by slowing activity in the root zone, including nitrogen uptake. A decrease in organic matter in the soil also leads to greater soil loss from wind and water erosion, and adversely affects the populations of beneficial flora and fauna.

Chemical fertilisers are likely to cause wider fluctuations in soil pH than organic manures. Ammonium fertilisers in particular are implicated in the acidification of soil and the consequent leaching of minerals such as calcium. There is growing evidence that high doses of synthetic nutrients—especially nitrogen in the form of nitrates—disrupt natural processes and adversely affect long-term soil fertility. Fertilisers speed up the process of decomposition, thereby further reducing the amount of organic matter in the soil.[2]

Cadmium and other trace toxic metals in synthetic fertilisers can accumulate in dangerous quantities in soils and crops. In Sweden, cadmium contamination of food is recognised as a growing problem. A recent study showed that synthetic fertilisers and industrial air pollution were the two most significant sources of cadmium on the farmland tested[3] (Table 3-1).

Table 3-1. Annual deposition of cadmium on Swedish farmland

Source	Cadmium (kg/yr)
Chemical fertilisers	5000
Air pollution	4000
Farmyard manures	800
Manure slurry	500
Chalk	100

Source: Swedish agricultural statistics yearbook, 1987

Much of the fertiliser that is applied to fields is, in fact, never taken up by the crops for which it is intended. Instead, it leaches into groundwater or is carried into surface waters, leading to eutrophication of lakes, streams and coastal waters, thereby threatening the lives of aquatic animals. It also ends up in drinking water (Figure 3-2)[4]. A recent study suggests that agriculture is the leading contributor to non-point-source pollution (pollution that cannot be traced to a specific source) in United States waters. It estimates that 50% of the nitrogen, 40% to 75% of the potassium and 5% to 25% of the phosphorus applied to agricultural lands ends up in surface or groundwater.[5]

Concentrations of oxides of nitrogen in drinking water throughout farming areas in Europe and North America exceed recommended safety levels.[6] Nitrate percolation into groundwater is especially alarming. Once an underground aquifer is contaminated, purification is possible only through natural processes, and these tend to be very slow. Although nitrogen pollution can come from a variety of sources—including feedlots, barnyards, septic systems and organic fertilisers—the huge increase in the use of chemical fertilisers is clearly a significant contributory factor.

Excess nitrogen from fertilisers (and poorly-managed livestock waste and crop residues) can also upset the balance of nitrogen in the atmosphere. There is always some volatilisation of nitrogen from fields, but the heavy nitrogen applications associated with industrial farming have led to increased emissions of nitrogen compounds that can contribute to acid rain. Some nitrogen compounds also absorb radiation reflected from the earth, and thus contribute to the problem of global warming.[7]

13

Figure 3-2
Nitrate concentration in Danish drinking water

Source: University of Tubingen

The readily available nutrients in synthetic fertilisers allow plants to absorb nutrients directly, thus short-circuiting the symbiotic relationship that has evolved between plants and mycorrhizae, the small fungal threads that penetrate a plant's roots.[8] According to French plant physiologist Chaboussou, the bypassing of this natural regulatory process can lead to a buildup of water-soluble sugars and free amino acids in plant tissues. These compounds are ideal food sources for many pests, making the plants far more susceptible to attack.[9]

Artificial fertilisers have also been shown to increase the water content of crops. Industrial farmers harvest more tonnes per acre than their predecessors partly because the retained moisture makes crops weigh more. When dry weights are compared, yields are much closer. Higher moisture content can lead to storage problems, such as increased susceptibility to moulding. Two recent studies—by the Institute of Development Studies at the University of Sussex, and by the United Nations Environment Programme—conclude that spoilage of food during storage in Southern countries is largely due to the increased water content of modern crops.[10]

Health Effects

Nitrogen pollution quite likely poses a threat to human health. When nitrates are ingested or cooked they can combine with amines to form nitrosamines—compounds that have proven to be carcinogenic in laboratory tests. A direct causal link between nitrate intake and cancer in humans has been difficult to prove in epidemiological studies. However, many studies do point to the need for caution and recommend a decrease in nitrate intake. Some segments of the population, especially the very young or aged, may be particularly susceptible, especially when exposed to other toxins such as pesticide residues.[11]

An Australian study found that babies born to mothers whose drinking water contained 5 to 15 parts per million of nitrates were three times more likely to suffer birth defects than babies born where nitrate levels were lower.[12] High nitrogen intake has also been linked to methemoglobinemia and cancer in the gastrointestinal tract, and may be toxic in other poorly understood ways.[13]

Methemoglobinemia is a nitrate-induced illness that deprives the brain of oxygen. Infants have been shown to be particularly susceptible, and the disease may be more prevalent than is commonly assumed. One study found 144 cases of methemoglobinemia in Minnesota farming communities, with 14 deaths in one 30-month period. A 1982 survey of physicians in the Big Sioux County region of South Dakota revealed a total of 80 recorded cases. A 1981 survey in the same region found that 29 percent of the wells tested exceeded the legal standard for nitrate concentration.[14]

Pesticides: The Deadly Solution

Modern agriculture relies heavily on the use of chemical pesticides to control crop loss from insects, animals and microorganisms. Pesticides have revolutionised farming techniques and have played a central role in the shift from small-scale diversified agriculture towards industrial monocropping. From a narrow perspective, their input might seem wholly beneficial. However, it is now widely known that chemical pesticides pose serious hazards both to the environment and to human health. Moreover, as target pests mutate and build up resistance, the pesticides become less and less effective. Over the course of time, more applications and stronger chemicals are required to keep pests in check. The end result is a spiral of destruction.

Environmental Effects

The environmental impact of pesticides begins in the manufacturing process. For example, one tonne of DDT produces two tonnes of toxic sludge as well as corrosive and toxic waste waters. As yet there is no safe disposal method for this waste, and current research programmes appear incapable of providing the necessary solutions.

Many pesticides persist in the environment long after application, causing damage to different life forms as they move through an ecosystem. In addition, some pesticides tend to accumulate in the bodies of animals. As these animals become prey to animals higher in the food chain, pesticides undergo a process known as 'biomagnification'—the higher an animal is on the food chain, the higher its concentration of pesticide. This effect was first noticed in the bald eagle and other predatory birds. DDT concentrations in the birds' bodies reached the level where the shells of the eggs they produced were too weak to prevent breakage in the nest. Although DDT has been banned in most countries in the North, it is still used in many parts of the South. Other broad spectrum biocides, particularly organochlorine compounds, exhibit similar characteristics to DDT, and are still in widespread use around the world. A large number of other pesticides have been proven to alter the structure and function of both terrestrial and aquatic ecosystems far from the point of application.[1] Dead fish and birds are common in areas polluted by agricultural runoff.

Table 4-1 Maximum pesticide concentrations found in samples of Swedish stream waters, 1985 - 1987

	Max concentration (μg/l)		Max concentration (μg/l)
Herbicides		*Fungicides*	
Atrazine	6.0	Metalaxyl	1.3
Bentazone	0.5	Propiconazole	1.2
Cyanazine	0.7		
2,4-D	0.9	*Insecticides*	
Dichlorprop	16.0	Endosulfan	0.1
MCPA	8.0	Fenitrothion	0.1
Mecoprop	6.0	Lindane	0.6
Metazachlor	7.0	Permethrin	0.6
Simazine	1.1	Pirimicarb	3.7
Terbuthylazine	0.7		

Source: Kreuger and Brink, 1988

More serious still is the problem of water contamination. Groundwater in five American states was recently found to contain traces of the highly toxic Aldicarb—despite laboratory and field tests performed by its manufacturer, Union Carbide, which had supposedly proved the pesticide would break down soon after application.[2] Wells in California have been found to contain DDT, aldrin, dieldrin, lindane, parathion, heptachlor, chlordane, toxaphene and 2,4,5-T.[3] One Swedish study found traces of 17 pesticides in streams during the agricultural season[4] (Table 4-1).

Pesticide contamination of groundwater is particularly disturbing because there is no known method for speeding up natural purification processes, which may take many years or even decades. Since chemicals travel very slowly through soil, water will continue to be polluted long

17

after the use of the chemicals has stopped. Some of the pesticides found in California wells, in fact, had been banned years earlier. Similar effects have been noted in other industrialised countries.[5]

Although pesticides are generally very effective at controlling pests in the short term, their performance declines over the years. Many pests quickly develop resistance to specific chemicals, and maintain that resistance even when dosages are increased.[6] In 1957, there were twenty-five species of arthropods that were resistant to at least one form of insecticide. By 1980, however, the United Nations Food and Agriculture Organisation estimated that the number of resistant species had risen to over 430. It is still rising today. Pesticides that were initially helpful in controlling malaria-bearing mosquitos are becoming increasingly ineffective, and the incidence of malaria in India and other countries is steadily rising.[7]

In the long term, pesticides often exacerbate the problems they were designed to solve. Many pesticides are blanket biocides that kill creatures other than the target pest, including its natural predators. When the populations of insects, birds and reptiles that once kept a pest in check have been eliminated or weakened, pests frequently return in greater numbers than were initially present. Alternatively, removing one pest merely opens the door to another. Mites were never a problem on orange trees until their natural predators were eliminated by pesticides aimed at a different problem.[8]

Pesticides can also lead to imbalances in plant metabolism, result-ing in the disruption of protein synthesis and the buildup of free amino acids within the plant. Such buildups have been shown to attract pests. Once again, pesticides actually add to the problem they were meant to alleviate.[9]

Health Effects

Beginning on the floor of the pesticide factory, pesticides pose a significant threat to human health. Many workers at a DPCP plant in California became sterile in the 1970s, while at an organophosphate pesticide facility in Texas, workers exhibited a wide range of troubling symptoms, including a lack of coordination and slurred speech.[10] These cases occurred in a country which has relatively tight safety regulations.

The situation is much worse in the less industrialised countries, where regulations are less strict or are poorly enforced.

Accidents in manufacturing plants are extremely dangerous and can be deadly. In 1984, a malfunction at the Union Carbide plant in Bhopal, India, killed thousands of people outright and maimed tens of thousands more. While this has been the most serious accident so far, it has not been the only one. The widespread dioxin contamination of the area around Seveso, Italy, and the severe contamination of the Rhine following an accident at the Sandoz plant in Basel, Switzerland, are two other recent examples. Perhaps even more worrisome are the routine releases of toxic wastes from pesticide plants—events that do not make the newspapers. The Sandoz accident was followed by the deliberate release of toxics from other plants along the Rhine, including the BASF plant at Ludwigshafen.[11]

Every year, the health of millions of farm workers is directly threatened by pesticides. People working in the fields inhale poisons during and after application and ingest them in their food and water. Again, the situation is particularly severe in the South, where labels and warnings are often unintelligible, and where relatively few workers are provided with the recommended protective equipment. However, even when manufacturers' instructions are followed precisely, poisoning is still common. In 1983 the United Nations Economic and Social Committee for Asia and the Pacific estimated that between 400,000 and 2,000,000 farmers worldwide are poisoned by pesticides each year, 20,000 to 40,000 of whom die as a result.[12] Another estimate suggests that as many as 300,000 farm workers in the United States alone may be suffering from pesticide-related illnesses.[13]

Direct causal links between pesticide exposure and subsequent long-term illness are extremely difficult to establish. However, the evidence is mounting. Out of 426 chemicals named in 1988 by the Ministry of Agriculture, Fisheries, and Food as ingredients in pesticides cleared for use in England, 164 had been implicated in causing cancer, genetic mutations, irritant reactions, or reproductive problems ranging from impotency to birth defects.[14] A 1986 National Cancer Institute study reported that farmers exposed to herbicides—especially 2,4-D—for more than twenty days per year were six times as likely to develop non-Hodgkins lymphoma, a cancer of the lymphatic system.[15] In the prime agricultural region of the San Joaquin Valley of California, where 35% of the wells are contaminated with DPCP, the State Department of Health Services found an increased mortality rate for stomach cancer, the primary site for tumour induction in animals used in testing DPCP.[16] In the small farm community of McFarland, California, thirteen children have developed cancer since 1981, and six have died; miscarriages, fetal deaths and low birth weights are common. A definitive causal link has not been established, but pesticide contamination in the region is a likely factor.[17] Other recent studies link agricultural chemicals to an increase in birth defects.[18]

Everyone eating food grown with chemical pesticides is potentially at risk. Even at supposedly safe levels, pesticides can build up within the human body and may contribute to serious health problems, such as cancer and birth defects. Many pesticides and their metabolites, especially chlorinated hydrocarbons such as DDT, build up in human fat tissue. Scientists are finding higher and higher levels of pesticides in people throughout the world. The effects are poorly understood, but the increased use of pesticides and other industrial chemicals has been followed by increased cancer rates. Since chronic health problems are usually slow in developing, it may well be that the most serious effects of pesticide contamination are yet to come.

Pesticide use in the less industrialised parts of the world is particularly disturbing. Seventy percent of the pesticides used in India are banned or severely restricted in the West. Although regulations on permissible levels in food do exist, they are poorly enforced. A recent survey of vegetables in a Delhi market revealed pesticide residues twenty times above legal limits, while a World Health Organization (WHO) survey in India found 50% of samples contaminated. In a survey in the state of Punjab, DDT and BHC, both banned in the West, were found in all seventy-five samples of human milk.[19]

Nor is pesticide use confined to agriculture. Herbicides and insecticides are commonly used in parks, city streets and gardens. People have even died from reactions to herbicides applied to golf courses. Defoliants used by the United States in the Vietnam War, similar to products now in commercial use, caused high rates of sterility, birth defects and cancer. Researchers found that children living in homes where household and garden pesticides were used were seven times more likely to develop childhood leukemia than those growing up in pesticide-free homes.[20]

Testing Pesticide Safety: Tricky Business

The long-term health effects of pesticides, which include carcinogenicity, mutagenicity and teratogenicity, are very difficult to assess. Since it is impossible to keep controlled subjects over the extended time period required to track chronic health effects, pesticide toxicology is a very inexact science. The effect of pesticides on humans must be extrapolated from studies of animals or animal cells. In the most common type of test, high doses of pesticides are given to mice or rats over a period of several months to years. The incidence of cancer or birth defects observed in the animals is then translated into expected cancer and birth defect rates for humans. The entire exercise, however, is filled with uncertainties:

- how can the physiological differences between test animals and humans be accounted for?
- how accurate are determinations of the effects of low pesticide doses based on studies of relatively high doses?
- how is a safe threshold established below which there are no effects?
- how can additive effects and synergies among toxins be accounted for?
- how can the variability caused by personal characteristics such as age, sex, and metabolism be determined?

These uncertainties make it very difficult to formulate regulations that will protect farm workers and the public. It is also impossible to determine the exact levels of pesticides to which people will be exposed (whether in the fields or in residues in foods). Weather, work practices, physical characteristics and diets all affect exposure rates, and all vary greatly.

Animal studies are expensive, and government regulators have had to rely on information supplied by the pesticide manufacturers. The tests required to register a pesticide have become more demanding, but thousands of pesticides that were first registered in the 60s and 70s are still in use and have not been retested.[21] Manufacturers have a large financial interest in registering pesticides, and several corporations have been caught falsifying data. Even in the countries with the strictest regulations, consumers remain unprotected from the effects of 'inert' ingredients mixed with the active pest-killing agent. In the US, manufacturers do not even have to reveal what is mixed with the active ingredient.

Economic Considerations

Economically, pesticides are a liability. New pesticides tend to be more expensive to develop and produce than the old ones they replace, because of the greater complexity of modern chemicals and the more rigorous testing required to meet new safety standards. It is, therefore, a reasonable assumption that prices will continue to rise.

In the industrialised world, concern over the impact on human health and the environment has led to the banning of many pesticides and the strict regulation of others. However, these chemicals represent a highly profitable, multi-billion dollar industry to the companies which manufacture and sell them. These multinational corporations promote pesticide use throughout the world, using sophisticated advertising campaigns and promotional offers to governments and farmers while obscuring information about the harmful side effects of their products.[22] Governments are often loathe to enforce existing regulations—let alone make the regulations tighter—for fear of upsetting these powerful economic interests. Even DDT was banned only after it had become largely ineffective. Meanwhile, the vast majority of pesticides marketed in the US have not been reassessed according to the latest standards.[23]

Multinational corporations still manufacture and export large quantities of pesticides whose use is banned in their country of origin.[24] Ironically, many of the pesticides used in the South are applied to export crops, so as to produce blemish-free products and to prevent spoilage during shipping. Citizens of rich countries end up ingesting pesticides that their own governments have banned.[25]

What Goes Around...Comes Around

The United States produces between 100 and 150 million pounds of pesticides which are considered too dangerous for use within the country's borders. These chemicals are exported for use in other nations with less stringent environmental safeguards. Yet these same banned and restricted agricultural chemicals find their way to the dinner table in homes all across the United States, in the form of residues on imported beef, cheese and vegetables. While inspectors at US borders check food imports for certain chemicals, they are only able to sample 1-2% of all shipments, and test for less than 40% of the pesticides on the market. In many cases, pesticides which cannot be legally used in the US—but which are manufactured domestically and exported overseas—are among those for which inspectors do not test.

According to US Department of Agriculture figures for 1990, illegal residues on imported food were four times as common as residues on domestic foods. It is not known how much of this contamination originated from pesticide factories operating within the US.[26]

Animal Husbandry: Farm as Factory

T he way we raise animals has been transformed by industrialisation. Production has become highly centralised and animals are treated as just another industrial product. Many meat and dairy products in the industrialised countries come from factory farms in which the goal is to fatten animals as quickly as possible. As a result, one third of the world's grain is now fed to animals, mostly in rich countries.

Animals in factory farms are closely confined to prevent movement and promote rapid weight gain. In the UK, more than half of the 58 million broiler chickens are kept in flocks of 100 thousand or more; 750 thousand breeding sows are confined throughout pregnancy in small cement-floored stalls; and as many as 200 thousand calves per year die of stress-related diseases.[1] Forced to live in environments that thwart every natural instinct, animals literally go crazy: chickens must be debeaked to keep them from pecking each other to death, and confined pigs exhibit neurotic behavior such as complete immobility, constant motion, or attacks on other pigs. Confinement in spaces so small that animals cannot even turn around, much less exercise, leads to deformities of bones, joints, and muscles. The short life of factory animals is characterised by constant fear and pain.[2]

To keep animals alive in close confinement requires massive and continual doses of drugs. This practice has resulted in new, antibiotic-resistant strains of bacteria (see, for example, Figure 5-1)[3]. These strains can infect humans as well as animals, and are very difficult to treat. Ringworm and salmonellosis, both transferable to humans, are an increasing problem.

Animal = Machine

The trade journals urging farmers to adopt modern industrial methods make it clear that animals should be thought of as machines rather than sentient beings:

"Forget the pig is an animal. Treat him just like a machine in a factory. Schedule treatments like you would lubrication. Breeding season like the first step in an assembly line. And marketing like the delivery of finished goods."
—*Hog Farm Management, September 1976*

"The breeding sow should be thought of, treated as, a valuable piece of machinery, whose function is to pump out baby pigs like a sausage machine."
—*National Hog Farmer, March 1978*

"Estrus control will open the doors to factory hog production. Control of female cycles is the missing link to the assembly line approach."
—*Farm Journal, January 1976*

"Each cow is placed in a contraption called a 'Unicar' which is a kind of cage on wheels that moves along a railway line. The cages, with cows in them, spend most of their time filed in rows in a storage barn. Two or three times a day, the farmer pushes a button in the milking parlor. Rows of cows then move automatically up to the milking parlor like a long train. As they go, their car wheels trip switches which feed, water, and clean the cars. After milking, the cows, still in the cages, roll back to the storage area."
—*Farm Journal, December 1971*

"The modern layer is, after all, only a very efficient converting machine, changing the raw material—feedstuffs—into the finished product—the egg—less, of course, maintenance requirements."
—*Farmer and Stockbreeder January 1962*

(Source: Robbins, 1987)

Because animals given feed laced with antibiotics have been found to gain weight faster than those on regular feed, farmers now routinely add antibiotics to feed. Almost half the antibiotics used in the United States are fed to farm animals, and show up as residues in meat.[4]

Figure 5-1
Development of resistance to streptomycine
in *E. coli* bacteria in pigs

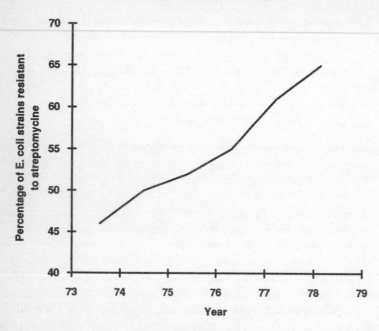

Source: Guillot *et al*, 1983

Other growth stimulants that can leave residues are now in common use. The widespread use of growth hormones is particularly worrying for human health. Although manufactured to mimic the substances produced within animals' bodies, synthetic hormones are sufficiently similar to human hormones that they can induce a variety of changes within human bodies, even in the small amounts left as residues in meat. While it is difficult to establish precise cause-and-effect connections, there is mounting evidence that hormone traces in meat have been a primary factor in lowering the age of puberty, and have caused children to develop sexual characteristics prematurely. Hormonal imbalances related to diet may also be implicated in the growing incidence of sexual disorders in adults.[5]

Despite all the drugs and attempts to control their environments, many of the animals are diseased when brought to the slaughter houses. Over eighty percent of the pigs in the United States have pneumonia, and at least fifty percent suffer from stomach ulcers at the time of slaughter. Beef with cancers and other diseases are common in the slaughter house. Only a small fraction of the meat is rejected, because rules on the frequency and mode of inspection favour the meat packing industry.[6]

Slaughterhouses often use inhumane methods. Rather than being killed outright, animals are stunned by electric shocks and actually bleed to death. Some scientists think that the animals' physiological response to the fear and stress at the time of death may leave hormonal residues in the meat that are harmful to humans.[7]

Like other types of modern agriculture, industrial meat production involves fewer and fewer farmers. Those who remain have become increasingly dependent on off-farm inputs and on the small number of corporations that control processing and marketing. Consider, for example, the production of broiler chickens. As a result of publicly-supported research into disease control and feed efficiency, large numbers of chickens can now be raised in smaller spaces and at a lower cost per chicken than in the past. To remain competitive, farmers have been forced to adopt the new techniques. In the process, they have become dependent on agribusiness to provide everything—the chicks themselves, the necessary feed, additives and pharmaceuticals, and the capital required for new buildings and equipment. Over the years, thousands of chick farmers have gone out of business, while most of the benefits of the new technology have gone to large corporations. Similar trends have occurred in beef and pork fattening and packing operations.[8]

In recent years, farm animals have been selectively bred to respond better to industrial techniques. Just as with food crops, this selective breeding results in a loss of genetic diversity. In the industrialised world, a handful of breeds comprise the great majority of beef and milk cows, making almost every herd dangerously susceptible to the same diseases.[9] The propagation of only a few breeds all around the world means that in most places the animals raised by farmers have not evolved and adapted to local conditions. This in turn means that the farmer must often import a whole range of inputs—from feed to medicines—to keep the animals healthy.[10] Highly-bred varieties of animals have been found to be more prone to illness and have shorter lives.

27

Factory farms are usually separated from farms growing crops. Moreover, animal manure collected from feedlots often cannot be used because the salt content is too high. The huge quantities of manure produced cause disposal problems. A modest size beef feedlot with 20,000 cows produces as much sewage as a city of 320,000 people, but rarely has even the most basic sewage treatment facilities. Meanwhile, run-off from the feedlots pollutes both surface and groundwater, as well as the atmosphere.[11] One study estimated that ammonia evaporating from the Netherlands' highly intensive livestock industry is responsible for 30% of the acid rain in that country.[12] The stench from intensively-housed animals can be smelled far from the feedlot.

Mechanisation: The Technological Treadmill

O ne of the most fundamental trends in industrial agriculture has been the replacement of human and animal labour by machines. Mechanisation has increased yields per unit of human labour input and has reduced the price of food. However, it has also resulted in the loss of many jobs and created a dependence on energy, capital and large-scale centralised technology.

Mechanisation encourages farming on a large scale. Small farmers are generally unable to use new technologies to full advantage and are compelled to either expand their operations or leave agriculture altogether. Of those who have chosen the former option, many have incurred large debts in order to finance the major capital investment required. This investment in specialised machinery encourages the abandonment of crop rotations, as farmers attempt to get the greatest use out of their expensive equipment by planting the same crop year after year.

Moreover, increased agricultural production has led to a general fall in prices, leaving millions of small farmers unable to meet mortgage payments, and forcing many into bankruptcy. Farmers have little choice but to embrace every technological innovation. However, when new technologies are widely adopted, total output generally rises, prices fall, and farmers find themselves worse off than before. This vicious cycle has been labelled the 'technological treadmill'.

Heavy agricultural machinery has produced significant problems of its own. In addition to causing serious accidents, it poses a very real threat to the land. Soil is compacted into permanent furrows, which then act as water channels, resulting in decreased absorption and increased erosion. Additionally, a layer of compacted subsoil known

29

as 'plough pan' can form over the years just below the level of soil turned over in ploughing. The compacted layer inhibits root growth and can trap water, leading to waterlogging. The problems associated with compaction have worsened as farm machinery has become heavier and the use of chemical inputs—requiring more passes across fields—has increased. Erosion is further encouraged when terraces and hedgerows are removed in order to make bigger fields that are more suited to large machines.

In many parts of the world, mechanisation goes hand-in-hand with large irrigation schemes. Over the last few decades, these schemes have enabled the amount of land available for agriculture to be substantially increased. However, the process has not been without cost. Degradation of the soil structure caused by industrial agriculture leads to a reduction in the soil's ability to retain moisture, and thus increases the demand for water. Arid land that has not previously supported agriculture often contains toxic salts that are mobilised by the application of water. Where evaporation rates are high, which is often the case in arid regions, these toxic elements concentrate in the upper layer of soil, eventually rendering it inhospitable to crops. In addition, irrigation may lead to inadequate drainage. It frequently raises the water table to the root zone and begins to inhibit growth.

These two phenomena—salinisation and waterlogging—plague irrigation schemes around the world. While not exclusively confined to large-scale projects, they are more common in the rapidly constructed (and often hastily planned) schemes of the post-war era than in traditional irrigation systems. To take just one example, salinisation and the buildup of toxic elements affects an increasingly large portion of the highly profitable agriculture of California's San Joaquin valley.[1]

In addition, a large number of irrigation projects are pumping groundwater at unsustainable rates. The huge Ogalla aquifer, which runs under eight American states, is being depleted fourteen times faster than it is being replenished.[2]

Topsoil Loss: The Hidden Crisis

The loss of fertile soil to wind and water erosion is a problem that has plagued agriculture since its inception. There is increasingly strong evidence, however, that erosion has been greatly exacerbated by modern industrial agriculture, and that the problem is steadily worsening. For example, erosion rates in the United States are significantly higher than even the crisis years of the 1930s 'Dust Bowl' era.[3] A recent study estimated that 44% of American farmland is losing soil above the tolerance level. The less arid farmlands of Europe are not losing as much soil to erosion, but losses are still significantly above the natural rate of soil formation. It takes between 120 and 400 years to form a centimetre of soil. Highly erodible lands may lose a centimetre per year, and the average for U.S. farmlands is one centimetre in eight years, clearly much higher than the rate of regeneration.[4] Worldwide it is estimated that 24 billion tonnes of topsoil are lost annually, roughly the same amount of topsoil on all of Australia's wheatland.[5]

The most fertile soil usually erodes first, reducing yields and leaving crops prone to drought, disease, and pest damage. Eroded soils are lower in organic matter and less able to hold moisture. More water runs off, further accelerating the erosion process. Soil in run-off clogs waterways, and the added nutrients and silt can lead to eutrophication and decimation of aquatic ecosystems. The useful life of reservoirs can be cut by 50% or more if the surrounding watershed is eroding rapidly. Small particles of soil can be carried hundreds of miles by the wind and can cause significant air pollution.

The switch from mixed-cropping systems that are based on crop rotations to intensive and specialised continuous-cropping is one of the primary reasons for increased erosion. The use of chemicals to the exclusion of organic inputs leads to a reduction in organic matter in the soil and a deterioration in soil structure, a critical factor in erosion rates. This translates directly into reduced yields. It has been shown that doubling organic matter (to 3.6% of total soil weight) raises corn yields by 25%.[6]

Altered management practices and the push to maximise production also contribute to erosion. Cultivating in the direction of the slope rather than along the contour, untimely cultivation, preparation of fine seed beds, and cultivation of grains on steeply sloped land with marginal soils have all increased erosion rates.[7]

Fossil Fuels: The True Cost

The increases in agricultural production of the last century have been made possible by tremendous increases in the use of fossil fuels, especially petroleum. Fossil fuels are used at every step of the agricultural cycle: for fertilisers and pesticides; for the manufacture and operation of machinery; and for transporting, processing and packaging farm produce. Since the beginning of this century the total energy input into a hectare of land planted in maize has increased by a factor of eight, while yields have increased by only three and a half (Figure 6.1). In 1983, the energy in just the nitrogen fertiliser applied to a hectare of maize exceeded *all* energy inputs to the same hectare of maize in 1945.[8]

Figure 6-1
Energy input in U.S. maize production
1910 – 1983*

Source: Pimentel & Pimentel, 1986

* Energy input includes energy embodied in human and animal labour, steel in machinery, fuels, fertilisers, seeds, pesticides, irrigation, drying, electricity and transport.

This heavy reliance on fossil fuels is quite unsustainable in the long term. Neither the supply nor the price of petroleum can be guaranteed, and indications are that the situation will only become more difficult as known sources are depleted. Even assuming that reserves could last indefinitely and that prices could be held at present levels, we would still have to face the massive environmental problems associated with the exploitation of fossil fuels. The true cost of our dependence on fossil fuels is not simply what we as consumers pay for them—not even what we as taxpayers pay, subsidising as we do the whole civil and military infrastructure required to ensure uninterrupted supply. The true cost must also take into account the life-threatening environmental damage—including acid rain, water pollution, habitat loss and global climate change—that our dependence on fossil fuels has caused. The United States energy industry, based on fossil fuels and nuclear power, currently enjoys a subsidy of 100 to 300 billion dollars per year, depending on how one does the accounting of tax breaks, environmental degradation, lost employment, and health costs.[9]

These are matters that conventional analysis of farming practices may not normally consider. Yet they are absolutely fundamental issues, and are direct consequences of the choices made by industrial society.

The Bigger Picture

I ndustrialisation has had a profound effect on what happens to food when it leaves the farm. Processing and transporting food have become major businesses in the industrialised countries, as people have been steered away from locally grown produce towards a vast array of processed foods which have often been transported great distances. On its way to the table, in fact, the food in the average American meal has travelled two thousand kilometres.[1]

Huge transport networks and cheap fossil fuels enable the countries of the North to enjoy an unprecedented variety in their diets throughout the year. However, the system is quite fragile—the average industrial city typically has food reserves for only a week or two—and is especially vulnerable to increases in the price of energy. The cost of environmental degradation caused by the wasteful use of fossil fuels in transporting food around the world is not reflected in the prices paid by consumers, but is instead put on credit for future generations to pay.

A relatively small number of highly integrated agribusiness corporations control most of the operations between farm and consumer. Trade in grain is perhaps the most concentrated part of the food industry: six companies handle 85% of world trade.[2] These corporations have been able to control the terms of trade with farmers. Cargill, a privately held company that controls 25% of the world grain market, reported a rise in profits of 66% in 1985-1986, a period in which sales were static and farmers experienced economic hardship.[3] Between 1980 and 1987 American farmers' earnings on the wheat in a box of cereal fell 33%, while the cost to the consumer of the same box of cereal *rose* 33%. Similarly, the relative value of farm produce compared to the cost of manufactured goods has declined. In 1973, an American farmer could buy a pickup truck with the gross earnings from the sale of 15 calves. In 1990, the same truck required the sale of

45 calves. In 1973, a tractor was worth bushels of wheat; in 1990, it was the equivalent of 13,577 bushels.[4]

The large corporations that control food processing have unceasingly promoted highly refined foods that yield a larger profit for the industry. Big business has systematically eliminated smaller operations, so that consumers now have a hard time finding locally-produced, relatively unprocessed food.

Much of the food produced by the industrial system is of poor nutritional quality. This is largely due to processing, which reduces natural nutritional content.

The average diet in industrial countries includes unhealthy quantities of fat, cholesterol, sugar and salt. Powerful interests representing the food processing industry and the meat, dairy and egg producers run expensive campaigns to try to obscure and counteract the evidence that the average industrial diet contributes significantly to the high incidence of heart disease, stroke, and cancer.[5]

Most processed products contain a wide range of chemical preservatives, colours and flavourings aimed at increasing their appeal. For example, chemicals are added to even such basic foods as chicken and pork in attempt to improve the bland flavour that characterises meat produced in factory farms, and to preserve it during lengthy periods of transportation and storage.

There is now growing evidence that long-term consumption of some of the chemicals used in food processing can lead to chronic health problems, including cancer. Food additives are still poorly regulated; in fact, only a small fraction have been adequately tested for their effects on human health. Although most industrial countries have laws that require all additives to be clearly marked on the label, consumers generally remain ill-informed and inadequately protected.[6]

Irradiating food is another method of food preservation that has been shown to increase shelf life but decrease food quality. Radiation kills the bacteria on food—but in the process it breaks down vitamins and produces a variety of carcinogenic substances. Although the process kills toxin-producing bacteria, it does nothing to get rid of toxins that may have already been produced. Since the rotting process is halted, there are no odours or tastes to warn people away from tainted food. Although irradiated food is not itself radioactive, irradiation necessitates the handling, transport and disposal of dangerous radioactive materials. The food processing industry is currently lobbying for increased use of irradiation by claiming that it will eliminate the need for many pesticides. In fact, irradiation will do nothing to eliminate the vast majority of pesticides, which are those used on the farm.[7]

The Decline of the Family Farm

One hundred years ago the majority of people in the industrialised countries were part of the farm economy; today the figure is typically around 3%. In the United States alone, 219,500 farms were lost between 1981 and 1986, their fields typically amalgamated into much larger farms.[8] Already squeezed by repayment schedules on loans for capital expenditures, small farmers are hit particularly hard by any downturn in the prices paid for their produce. Even a relatively minor drop in market prices can lead to bankruptcy.

In an attempt to stabilise the farm economy, governments in Europe, North America and Japan have regulated the prices of agricultural commodities. The results have been far from satisfactory. The subsidies upon which such policy depends have become a huge financial burden for governments and have helped large corporations more than small farmers. Moreover, the system has further eroded local control of agriculture and led to an array of quite absurd situations in which the short-term interests of individual farmers are at direct odds with the long-term interests of both society as a whole and the environment.[9] For example, U.S. farmers who rotate crops stand to lose eligibility for subsidies—a disincentive against a clearly beneficial practice.

The decrease in the number of small farms has led to the impoverishment of rural communities. Fewer farmers translates into reduced demand for goods and services provided by local institutions such as retail stores, schools, libraries and hospitals. Rural areas are being steadily depopulated, and the quality of life for those left on the land is declining.[10]

Life is not necessarily any better for those who leave farming in search of work in the towns and cities. In the past, such people were readily absorbed within expanding urban economies. Today, however, the situation is very different. Unemployment is now endemic in industrial society, and jobs that pay a wage on which one can live are increasingly hard to find.

Traditional agricultural methods depended on the experience and location-specific knowledge of the farmer. The family farm encouraged a sense of pride in one's work and promoted a concern that land and water resources should be passed on intact to the next generation. The industrialisation of agriculture has brought with it very different ideals, encouraging farmers to forsake values of husbandry in favour of efficiency and narrow financial expediency. Working practices are no longer determined to any great extent by personal experience but are instead imposed from the outside by the economics of mass production. In the words of Wendell Berry, 'Kindly use depends on intimate knowledge, the most sensitive responsiveness and responsibility. As knowledge (hence, use) is generalised, essential values are destroyed.'[11]

The implications of trends such as these can be far-reaching, affecting even personal and social values. A cross-cultural study of children from six quite different populations around the world (Okinawa, Philippines, Northern India, Kenya, Mexico and the United States) found that children who lived within the rural economy were more altruistic, less egotistical and less aggressive than their peri-urban or urban counterparts.[12]

Agriculture has become a highly capitalised industry. The investment per worker in agriculture is almost as great as in manufacturing. As a result, the whole nature of farming has undergone a profound change. As can be seen in Figure 7-1, prices farmers pay for inputs have risen much faster than the prices they receive for their produce.

The economic benefit of greatly increased production has been captured by the suppliers of inputs: seeds, fertilisers, pesticides, machinery and capital. In 1940 these operating expenses were 44% of gross income; by 1984 they had risen to 67%. Capital expenditures doubled their share and interest expenses tripled in the same period.[13]

Banks are reluctant to lend to farmers who do not follow 'normal' (i.e. chemical) methods, and insist that output be maximised in order to protect their investment in the short term. As a consequence, creditors are able to exert tremendous control over the whole agricultural system. Together with large food processors, they can largely determine which crops are grown and how. Inevitably, this control leans heavily in favour of larger-scale operations, and thereby serves to tighten the grip of corporate control.

Within socialist economies, the broad picture is essentially the same. Farmers have even less control over their livelihood, and central planning has inevitably led to an unecological and unsustainable use

37

of local resources. Just as in the West, urban-based bureaucrats have relentlessly pursued the goal of growth in production while ignoring broader social and environmental costs. Rural powerlessness and environmental degradation are just as much problems of the East as of the West.

Figure 7-1
Comparison of index of prices paid by U.S. farmers to index of prices farmers received for their produce

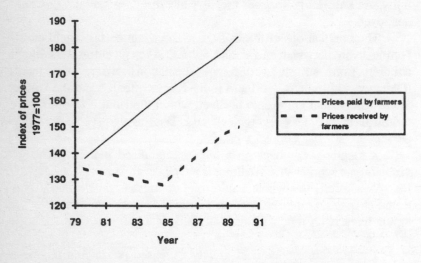

Source: U.S. Dept. of Agriculture, Agricultural Prices Annual Summary

The South: Exporting Food, Importing Poverty

Throughout the world the industrial model of agriculture is replacing a wealth of diverse traditional systems and bringing with it social, economic and ecological breakdown. For the non-industrialised parts of the world, the consequences are particularly severe. Their terms of international trade are unfavourable[14] and their towns and cities are even less able to accommodate rural 'refugees'—either in terms of physical infrastructure or employment possibilities—than those of their industrial counterparts. In many cases the imposition of industrial agriculture destroys existing and varied socioeconomic traditions that have proved themselves over centuries.

Development: Creating Urban Slums

The cities of the South are exploding. It's generally thought that this is merely a product of overall population growth. But the more fundamental cause is the process of 'development', which systematically pulls people away from the land into urban centres.[15] Investment in large-scale infrastructure—which forms the backbone of development—is inherently urbanising, and destructive of local economies and small-scale agriculture:

- modern *transportation* networks make it possible for large, distant corporations to compete with small local producers;
- for the sake of 'efficiency', the distribution of *energy* is highly centralised;
- Western-style *education* robs children of local knowledge and skills, forcing them instead to compete for scarce jobs in the urban economy.

Industrial agriculture is an integral part of the development 'package', and contributes directly to the problem of urbanisation. As Edward Goldsmith has pointed out,

Third World countries are being pressured to 'modernise' their agriculture—partly to satisfy IMF conditionalities, partly because the FAO, the agro-chemical industry and the farm machinery companies are pushing them to do so. This push towards industrial agriculture favours very large plantations, because small farms can't afford all the inputs required. The result is that small farmers are pushed off the land, and ultimately into the slums. For example, India has 800 million people, and 600 million still live off the land. If India adopts modern agriculture, which is what they are expected to do, the country will end up with farms of 500 acres and only 3% of the population producing food for everyone else. They'll be able to produce their food with 20 million people. But what do you do with the other 580 million? Shoot them? That would be the honest, the humane thing to do. But instead they'll be pushed into the slums.[16]

The Green Revolution, which was initially held up as a model of successful agricultural development, has now been widely discredited. Although new seeds and chemical fertilisers combined to raise yields significantly from previous levels, the overall environmental and social impacts have been disastrous. Looking back we can see that communities have been torn apart, human health threatened and environments degraded. Big landowners, encouraged by governments eager to acquire the hard currency needed for industrial development, have concentrated on producing crops for export, causing local food production to decline. In many cases the poor have become poorer and the rich richer. An International Labour Organisation study shows that while cereal production per capita and GNP per capita rose in South Asia during the 60s and 70s, there was also an increase in rural poverty.[17] Many of those who could not afford the new techniques have lost their land (and, consequently, the ability to grow their own food), only to become a further addition to the vast pool of surplus labour characteristic of the less industrialised countries of the world. Countless numbers of farmers have seen their standard of living eroded by exactly the same cost/price squeeze that is hurting small farmers in the North.[18]

The wealth of the North and its insatiable appetite for variety also adversely affects the poorer nations of the South. The Netherlands depends on 15-16 million hectares of cropland in other countries to supplement its own two million hectares, and the United Kingdom consumes the produce of two hectares abroad for every one farmed at home.[19] In 1982, Brazil devoted 8.2 million hectares to growing soya beans that were then exported to Europe as livestock feed. The same area could have produced sufficient protein in the form of black beans to feed 35 million people. The South exports more protein to feed livestock than comes back in food aid.[20] While in theory this trade benefits both North and South, it actually depresses local food production and leaves people dependent upon market forces beyond their control. Moreover, the benefits of this kind of trade tend to remain in the hands of the elite.

Biotechnology and 'Free' Trade: More of the Same

M any of the problems outlined in the preceding chapters are now quite widely recognised. However, the industrial system itself, which is the *root cause* of the problems, is rarely questioned. On the contrary, almost all official agricultural planning is a product of the same reductionist thinking and vested interests which have led to the situation that we face today. Far from offering solutions to the problems, the lastest trends are set to plunge us ever deeper into ecological and social crisis. Two developments are particularly worrying: the liberalisation of international trade and the emergence of new biotechnologies.

Trade and GATT

The increase of both regional and international trade is commonly seen as a means of raising living standards in both the North and South. The promise is that, by opening up new markets, all trading partners will be better off. In reality, however, the liberalisation of trade will be harmful to both the North and South. Large corporations will be allowed to exploit the cheap labour and lower environmental standards of the South. As a result, unemployment in the industrialised world will worsen, while in the South people will be even more rapidly pulled off the land to work as wage-slaves producing basic needs for the North. Such trends are extremely disturbing since these corporations lie outside the realm of democratic control, and in fact threaten to outstrip governments in their influence and power.

Furthermore, 'free trade' means more trade, and will inevitably lead to a dramatic increase in transport, which is why road-building is one of the highest priorities on government agendas today. This increase in transport will exacerbate a whole range of environmental problems, as well as furthering the breakdown of rural communities and local economies.

Ninety percent of the world's agricultural trade is governed by rules laid out in the General Agreement on Tariffs and Trade (GATT). An examination of the latest round of GATT negotiations, termed the Uruguay Round, makes the danger of liberalisation clear.

The implementation of a 'free trade' policy would mean the elimination of all subsidies to farmers. While in some respects this would be a positive step, the rapid and indiscriminate elimination of all subsidies would certainly force many smallholders out of business. Moreover, current free-trade proposals would outlaw as trade restraints many environmental programmes—such as reforestation projects, conservation programmes, and measures which make it possible for farmers to make a transition to environmentally sound farming methods.

Limits on exports and imports of agricultural products and raw materials are further obstacles to free trade that would be abolished. The United States, for example, recently challenged Indonesia's export ban on rattan, which had been enacted to protect a dwindling forest resource. Import quotas on raw materials are now used by poorer countries to protect local farmers from being wiped out by competition from industrialised countries. Under GATT, protection would be phased out entirely over 5 to 10 years, forcing farmers to use more intensive methods or go out of business.

Proponents of free trade are also seeking the 'harmonisation' of health and safety regulations—the so-called Sanitary and Phytosanitary Measures governing the use of additives and allowable levels of residues of pesticides and other toxins in food. International standards would be set by the Rome-based Codex Alimentarius—an international agency administered by the World Health Organisation—and the UN Food and Agricultural Organisation. Codex standards represent a lowest common denominator that is often much less strict than European or North American standards. For example, they would allow residues in food of some pesticides such as heptachlor, aldrin, and lindane that are 5,000% higher than US Environmental Protection Agency regulations. Codex has standards for only one-third as many contaminants as the EPA. Any local laws that were more restrictive than the international standard could be challenged as unfair restraint of trade. Given GATT's recent precedents—such as the ruling against US restrictions on imports of tuna caught by methods that kill dolphins—it is likely that a number of hard-won consumer protection measures could be overruled. European laws that protect animal welfare and outlaw the use of growth hormones in meat, and US laws such as the 'Delaney Clause' (which bans the use of proven carcinogens as food additives) and the 1990 Nutrition and Food Labeling and Education Act, would probably be declared illegal.[1]

Responsibility for setting health standards would be taken away from local and national governments and given to a small group of international bureaucrats operating in secrecy. Codex decisions are heavily influenced by lobbyists from major food-processing corporations, while consumer advocates are almost completely absent from their deliberations. Under current interpretations, no country could make health laws that would have an effect beyond its borders; any country proposing stricter standards would be required to prove to Codex's satisfaction that the rules were based purely on 'sound science', and that the results could not be achieved in a way that was less restrictive to trade. These rules would virtually eliminate the possibility of citizens' initiatives to protect health and improve food quality.

Biotechnology

The revolution in biotechnology of the last two decades is beginning to reshape agriculture. New techniques include the transplanting of genetic information from one organism into another (gene splicing), the reproduction of plants from the tissue of parent plants (tissue culture techniques) and the use of engineered bacteria and enzymes to synthesise food products. These technologies are already furthering the trend towards corporate control, and will have dire consequences for small farmers producing for the international market. In addition, they represent a severe threat both to human health and the natural environment.

Unlike the research and development at the international crop breeding centres that led to the Green Revolution, the new biotechnologies are firmly in the hands of private corporations. Application is directed by the need for short-term returns on investments. There is tremendous pressure on scientists to find commercially viable applications for their research. Even basic research paid for with public funds is influenced by the profit motive, as universities have started to promote joint ventures between professors and private interests. The goal is to retain bright researchers, but the private gain of the investors and researchers will be met first, often at the expense of the public.[2]

The successful propagation by tissue culture techniques of a high-yielding oil palm will allow agribusiness to start large plantations even more quickly and cheaply. This will drive out small producers, such as the many family coconut operations in the Philippines and small groundnut producers in West Africa.[3] Large plantations of genetically identical plants will give rise to all the same problems associated with industrial monocultures and will encourage the long-term erosion of genetic diversity.

The forces of GATT and biotechnology overlap in the attempt by Northern countries to extend conventions on intellectual property rights (including the patent and copyright systems) to capture the biological resources of the South. Traditional varieties of seeds, propagated and bred by indigenous people over many centuries, are now widely expropriated by Northern corporations without compensation to the country of origin. Hybrids and genetically altered seeds are patented and then sold back to the South. Under current GATT proposals, once a plant variety was patented it would be illegal for farmers to propagate new plants without paying compensation to the holder of the patent. In other words, farmers would be obliged to give way to the interests of the multinationals.

The focus of the new biotechnologies is on adapting food production to the needs of industry. Current projects include engineering fruits and vegetables to better withstand industrial harvest, transport, and processing techniques, rather than enhancing nutrition or taste.

Among the first products of the biotechnological revolution to reach the market were seeds engineered for greater resistance to specific herbicides and pesticides (see Table 8-1). The engineered resistance allows farmers to use herbicides on a greater number of crops and in larger doses than before. There are tremendous financial incentives for the large multinational chemical companies—which also control many seed companies—to use genetic engineering to to design seed/chemical packages whose components cannot be used separately. It is unlikely that the current system will lead to the decrease in chemical use that genetic engineering proponents promise. In fact, the marketing of seeds and chemicals as a package will leave farmers fewer choices, as independent seed companies are forced out of business and less profitable seeds that do not respond well to herbicide application are dropped from production.[4]

Genetic engineering makes possible the synthesis of animal hormones that stimulate growth and milk production. Lower priced hormones will increase their use, and set off another round of the technological treadmill as larger farmers adopt the innovations and drive smaller farmers out of business. The long-term consequences of hormone use on animal and human health are unknown, but there is mounting evidence of negative side-effects.

Table 8-1
Corporations engaged in research to increase herbicide tolerance in crops

Seed Corporations	Location	Pesticide Corporations	Location
Pioneer Hi-Bred	USA	Bayer	FR German
Sandoz-Hilleshog	Switzerland	Ciba-Geigy	Switzerlan
Upjohn	USA	ICI	UK
La Farge/Rhone-Poulenc	France	Rhone-Poulenc	France
ICI	UK	Dow/Elanco	USA
Dekalb-Pfizer	USA	Monsanto	USA
Ciba-Geigy	Switzerland	Hoechst	FR German
		Dupont	USA

Source: *Biotechnology's Bitter Harvest*

Bovine growth hormone (BGH) is one of the first synthetic hormones to be proposed for marketing. Supporters of BGH claim it will greatly increase the efficiency with which cows assimilate feed, and will increase milk production by up to 30% per cow. Opposition to marketing approval has centred on the economic effects. Since there is already a surplus of dairy products in the United States and Europe, widespread adoption of the new technology will almost certainly force more dairy farmers, especially the smaller operators, out of business. The non-economic side-effects of BGH are just starting to be understood. In a recent study in Vermont (the results of which were leaked against the wishes of study sponsor Monsanto), cows injected with BGH were compared to cows cared for conventionally. The cows given the hormones were found to be ill more frequently, had shortened milking lives, and gave birth more often to dead and deformed calves.[5] There is also concern over the health effects of BGH residues in milk.

It is also now possible to transfer human growth genes into cattle, sheep and pigs, to stimulate more rapid growth and weight gain. The long-term effects of this type of manipulation are unknown, although past experience has shown that the more 'efficient' animals tend to be less fit, and require precisely-controlled conditions to achieve maximum results.

New reproductive techniques, including genetic manipulation of embryos, will further denaturalise the breeding of animals. Scientists have already crossed distinct species, such as sheep with goats, to produce animal species that have never occurred naturally. The potential effects on genetic stocks and natural systems are extremely worrying.

The biotechnological revolution has also introduced new forms of pesticides. Bacteria are cultivated to produce large amounts of toxins, and are then killed, fixed, and applied as a topical insecticide. This process is more effective and longer lasting than ordinary toxins, and the dead bacteria do not spread. Viruses are also being manipulated for use as pesticides. However, such viruses could produce more potent and widespread effects than intended or even spread out of control. In addition, pest populations can still develop resistance to these pesticides, necessitating newer and stronger preparations. The long-term consequences of releasing biologically engineered organisms into the environment are poorly understood. Environmental disruptions could occur at any level of the ecosystem. If such disruptions affected energy flow or nutrient cycling, they could be extremely difficult to reverse.[6]

These techniques represent the latest step in a long series of manipulations of nature that reduce diverse and complex ecosystems to ever greater uniformity and simplicity. As with earlier interventions of the industrial system, short-term benefits hide potentially disastrous long-term social and environmental consequences. While researchers are now beginning to be able to transfer individual genes from one plant to another, they are far from understanding how groups of genes interact, or which genes are actually responsible for complex plant processes. Genetic manipulation implies inherent uncertainty. Many of the manipulations may be benign, but the potential for environmental disaster is high: once a living organism is released from the laboratory, it is all but impossible to recall or eliminate it.

The ability to assess the risks associated with the release of engineered organisms lags far behind the ability to manipulate genes. Relatively little is known about the complex interactions among plants, bacteria, viruses, and insects in agricultural ecosystems. Some scientists estimate that as many as 80% of soil microbes have yet to be cultured and 90% do not have names. Scientists do not know why some species of microbes multiply in nature and others do not, or how organisms establish themselves. Yet biotechnology research is heavily concentrated on microorganisms, because these are the easiest to manipulate genetically.[7]

The ability of human beings to create life-forms never before found in nature presents deeply disturbing ethical questions. At the very least, manipulative power of this magnitude demands widespread, soul-searching public debate—a debate that is notably absent.[8]

The New Agriculture:
Back to Basics

The Context of Ecological Agriculture

T he wide range of problems associated with industrial agriculture—whether environmental, social or economic—are the result not only of specific practices and policies, but of fundamental flaws in the way we look at the world. By the same token, the move towards more ecological agricultural practices will necessarily involve a reassessment of the assumptions underlying modern industrial society.

A good starting point is a re-examination of the concept of wealth. What do we mean by prosperity? What are the factors that contribute to a society's well-being?

In stark contrast with the conventional view, which measures wealth almost exclusively in terms of *money*, the ecological perspective is rooted in broader concerns to do with the health of the planet and its people. Whatever a nation's GNP may be, it cannot reasonably consider itself 'rich' if it is steadily degrading the resource base upon which its very existence depends, if large numbers of its citizens have no meaningful work, if crime and drug abuse are rapidly escalating, or if the poor are getting progressively poorer while the rich are getting progressively richer. True wealth is not to be found in balance sheets—certainly not the type of balance sheets we use today—but in the more subtle, less easily measurable relationships which link us to one another and to the earth. We need to ask two questions: first, is our way of life *sustainable*, for both the North *and* the South; and second, does it lead to human well-being?

In the case of industrial society, the answer to both of these questions is a resounding '*no*'. Our way of life is totally dependent on the rapid use of finite, non-renewable resources, and is therefore quite *un*sustainable. And it would be even less sustainable if the South were to use resources at anything approaching the rate of the North. So far as the question of human happiness is concerned, almost all the non-monetary indicators—crime, divorce, child abuse, suicide—show a clear trend from bad to worse.

In order to bring about more sustainable and satisfying patterns of living, we need to better understand the natural world and our relationship to it. We need to move away from our mechanistic view of the world to a more *holistic* and *systemic* science. Natural systems are not reducible to component parts; they do not operate according to linear laws of cause and effect. Rather, they take the form of infinitely complex webs, constantly moving and changing. What is more, no two ecosystems are the same. In nature, there are no 'standards': each forest, river, and field is unique.

We urgently need to value and nurture the particular characteristics of local ecosystems. We must learn to adapt the way we work the land so as to acknowledge the needs of nature, rather than manipulating nature to suit the needs of the economy.

This in turn requires a sense of humility: the very opposite of the collective arrogance which is so characteristic of modern industrial culture. When we stop trying to dominate nature, and strive instead to attune ourselves to natural rhythms, we will come to realise how little we understand the broader workings of the world, how little control we really have. In the face of such ignorance, such uncertainty, we will be compelled to proceed cautiously.

If it is to be sustainable, agriculture needs to be based on a radically different set of principles and structures from those which characterise the industrial model. In place of the specialist, we need to encourage the *generalist*: one who looks not at just one small part of the picture in isolation, but who is concerned to understand the full range of consequences—ecological, economic and social—which necessarily result when human beings interact with the environment.

Ecological agriculture reflects the *diversity* of nature. In the natural world, monocultures do not exist. On the contrary, even the simplest ecosystems contain a wide variety of animal and plant life. The planting of large areas of single crops is profoundly unnatural and inherently unstable. By contrast, diversity means stability and security.

Nature-based farming methods also imply smaller scale, and encourage a *decentralisation* of political and economic power. Rather than relying on chemical inputs produced by large multinational corporations, ecological agriculture is based on the recycling of nutrients on the farm itself.

52

The promotion of a decentralised system of agriculture would allow massive cuts in expenditure on transport insfrastructures. With the emphasis on local production for local consumption, both pollution and packaging could be greatly reduced, and people would be able to eat fresher, healthier food, free from all the preservatives and other processing agents which today's absurdly wasteful practices require.

Ecological agriculture also encourages a greater degree of individual responsibility. Farming on a small scale and within a relatively 'closed' system allows farmers to see more directly the consequences of their actions, which in turn promotes a greater sense of care—both for the land and for the community. Ultimately, the living experience of interdependence with the land and one's neighbours provides a richness to life which is sorely missing from modern agribusiness.

Learning from the Past

I ndustrial farming techniques have become so dominant in the North that it is easy to forget that chemical agriculture has gained widespread acceptance only during the last forty years. What's more, hundreds of millions of farmers—mostly in the South— still farm much the way their ancestors did. These traditional systems are, in fact, the only time-tested models of sustainable agriculture. Although specific methods vary greatly from place to place, agricultural practices that have maintained or enhanced the local resource base share many general organisational principles.[1]

Adaptation to Specific Ecosystems

Traditional systems often closely mimic the productivity, stability, and sustainability of the surrounding ecosystem.[2] For example, the forest gardens and swidden plots of the humid tropics resemble the lush forests which preceded them. The continuous cover of diverse plant life stores most of the nutrients while protecting the garden from the damaging effects of intense sun and rain. Farmers introduce plants useful to humans in a sequence that mirrors the natural succession of wild annuals, herbaceous perennials, trees and vines.

In arid regions, such as the deserts of the southwest United States and northern Mexico, agricultural practices have evolved that make use of a wide variety of plants adapted to temperature and moisture extremes. Papago Indian farmers locate their fields where they will gather water and nutrients brought by runoff from sporadic but intense rains. Planting decisions accomodate local patterns of wind, rain, and temperature. Deep-rooted nitrogen-fixing trees are left in fields to fertilise them and protect small plants from the sun. Making full use of their ecosystem's potential, the Papagos also gather wild and semi-wild plants, which provide an important part of their diet.[3]

Farmers in the lowlands of China's Zhujiang (Pearl) River delta have adapted well to the features of the marshy, flood-prone region. Their mixed agriculture/aquaculture has transformed the area into a patchwork of dikes and ponds that yield fish, sugar cane, mulberry, silkworms, pigs, vegetables, and fruits. Crops grown on the dikes feed animals and humans, while household and animal waste, crop residues and cuttings from the dikes feed carp in the ponds. The nutrient-rich mud of the pond bottoms, excavated during maintenance, fertilises the dike-top fields. The system provides a rich and varied diet, as well as cash crops such as silk, fish, and sugar cane.[4]

Diversity On the Farm

Instead of fields of a single species of plant, traditional systems often use numerous crops simultaneously, or rotate them sequentially in a given field. Inter-cropping and polyculture are very efficient ways of using land, since they allow intensive production despite limited land resources. Farmers in Zacatelco, Tlaxcala, Mexico, for example, grow six or more crops simultaneously in the same field. In the first phase, chick-peas, broad beans and peas are planted. In the second phase, maize, beans and squash are planted in the furrows. After the harvest, plants of the first phase are removed (and used for fodder) to expose the second-phase seedlings. The broad beans and maize provide support for the peas and climbing beans, and the legumes add nitrogen to the soil. This system provides a continuous and varied food supply over a long growing season.[5]

In addition to a varied diet, a diversity of crops contributes to self-reliance in fuel, fodder, fertiliser, medicine and fibre. Homegardens in West Java, for example, include over 120 species of plants, filling at least eight different purposes (Table 10.1).[6] In Sri Lanka, traditional highland gardens may contain over twenty tree species as well as numerous shrubs, vines and ground plants.[7]

Planting a diversity of crops is an effective strategy for mitigating the risks of crop failure. If one crop or variety fails due to pests, disease or adverse weather conditions it is likely that at least some of the other crops will survive. Genetic variety within a specific crop is often purposefully guarded and nurtured. Farmers in the harsh climate of the Peruvian Andes plant as many as 46 varieties of potatoes in a half hectare plot.[8] Natives of the American Southwest physically separated corn varieties to prevent cross-pollination and mixing of strains.[9] Farmers in many cultures exchange seeds among villages to ensure continued vigour and pest resistance.

Table 10-1. Distribution of plant species in traditional system of West Java, Indonesia

Main function of plants	Mixed garden/tree plantation		Homegarden	
	# of species	percent	# of species	percent
Ornamentals	8	7	47	37
Medicinals	5	4	8	6
Spices	5	4	6	5
Vegetables	15	13	18	14
Cash crops	7	6	6	5
Fruits	20	18	22	17
Additional food crops	5	4	8	6
Building materials and firewood	47	42	12	9
TOTAL	112		127	

Source: Christanty et al, 1986

Practices that augment the natural resistance of plants are often supplemented by other agricultural techniques. In Sri Lanka, for example, peasants use a number of mechanical methods—including water-powered drums to scare pests away, sweeping plants with specially gathered branches, drawing a gummed rope across fields, and throwing sand at crops to remove harmful insects. Various herbal concoctions are applied to plants (e.g. mimosa, mangosa, and asafetida leaves combined with cow's urine as a general purpose insecticide).[10]

The success of such methods was summed up by Sir Alfred Howard, who came to India in 1905 as the Imperial Economic Botanist to the Government of India. Amazed to find the fields of peasant farmers free of pests and needing no insecticides or fungicides, he commented, 'I decided that I could do no better than watch the operations of these peasants and acquire their traditional knowledge as rapidly as possible.'[11]

Integration with Natural Cycles

The productivity of industrial farms is dependent on massive infusions of fossil-fuel based inputs. Traditional farms, in contrast, depend on locally-available nutrient and energy sources. Asian farmers, for example, have practised rice paddy cultivation for centuries without relying on imported inputs. Blue-green algae, which grow in the flooded fields, are the main source of nutrients. Buffalo or oxen not only provide traction power for ploughing: their manure fertilises the soil, and the pressure of their hooves helps to seal the paddy bottom. In some areas, nitrogen-fixing cowpeas or mung beans are sown into standing rice stubble as a source of nitrogen. The beans also reduce the damage caused by bean flies, thrips and leafhoppers by interfering with their ability to find hosts. Flocks of domesticated ducks and other birds feed on aquatic weeds, and fertilise the fields with their droppings. Fish raised in the paddies help control insects and add protein to the diet. In some areas, trees that fix nitrogen and bring up minerals from the sub-soil are grown in the paddy. Trees also help to stabilise dike walls, provide fodder, offer shade to workers, and attract bats and birds whose droppings further fertilise the fields.[12]

Like paddy culture, all long-lived agricultural systems have developed unique and often ingenious methods for ensuring a continuous supply of nutrients, controlling erosion, and managing water supplies. Raised-bed agriculture, for example, which was developed primarily in regions of Latin America with high water tables (but also practised in China and elsewhere) involves a system of elevated fields surrounded by water channels. Canals drain away excess water, provide habitat for beneficial plants and animals, and moderate temperature extremes. Muck, rich in nutrients, is dredged from the canals and used as fertiliser in the fields.[13]

Another common method of regenerating fertility is the management of flood waters so that nutrient-rich silt is deposited on fields. This method sustained the intensive cultivation of such areas as the Nile valley in Egypt (prior to the construction of the Aswan dam) and the Niger delta region of Mali. Flood waters can also be managed by use of numerous small check dams. Such systems are common throughout arid regions of Meso-america.

Farmers in mountainous regions must pay particular attention to the management of water and the control of erosion. Over the centuries, traditional farmers in many parts of the world have constructed

57

and maintained vast networks of terraces. Terraces slow runoff, help channel irrigation water, stabilise fragile soils, and make cultivation possible in otherwise unproductive areas. Terracing methods vary greatly, since they reflect local needs and materials. Rocks, trees, perennials, cut brush, and shaped earth are all used to form retaining walls.

Long-lived traditional irrigation systems also carefully provide for continued maintenance of the system, through desilting, repair of channels and upkeep of drains in fields prone to water-logging. On the Tibetan plateau in the Indian region of Ladakh, farmers with only hand tools have constructed irrigation canals kilometres long, sometimes traversing sheer rock faces. Water is the main constraint to food production in this arid region, and villages have worked out detailed plans for water distribution and cooperative repair of channels.

One of the more ingenious methods of bringing water to fields is the system of *galerías filtrantes* of Pueblo, Mexico. *Galerías* are tunnels that start below the water table, and then slope more gently than natural gradients so that eventually they intersect the surface. The ground water is free to flow to the surface where it then can be applied to the fields. The tunnels range in length from 100 metres to several kilometres. Although fairly costly to build and maintain, *galerías* allow the security of irrigated agriculture in an arid region of variable rainfall.[14]

Links to Local Community and Economy

Another common feature of traditional systems is that they have evolved in response to a wide range of criteria, not just the output of a few marketable crops. Traditional agriculture tends to be integrated with the social bonds of the community. Festivals and rituals are closely linked to the cycles of the agricultural year. Many traditional agricultural practices would not be possible without specific social practices to support them. For example, the annual desilting of the tanks and canals in Sri Lanka was also an important religious observance. Participation by all members of the village strengthened connections to each other and to the earth.

The study of traditional agricultural systems also highlights the vast differences between distribution systems in traditional and modern societies. While the great majority of societies engaged in the trade of agricultural produce, the exchanges took place locally, and were not purely 'economic' as they are today. Instead they tended to be embedded in social relations, reflecting a range of considerations—strengthening kinship ties, meeting reciprocal obligations, contributing to communal festivals and building inter-village alliances. Basic needs were met close to home through face-to-face exchange. Traditional economies generally ensured an adequate supply of nutritionally-balanced food for all members of society. Nutritional difficiencies are, in fact, much more likely in societies where people have lost control of their land—usually through integration into larger markets—than in traditional subsistence economies.[15]

Within the most industrialised countries of the North there are still agricultural communities which have successfully resisted the adoption of industrial technologies. Perhaps the best-known are the Amish, who emigrated from Europe to settle in tight-knit communities in the East and Midwest regions of the United States. As in traditional societies elsewhere, the Amish religion, sense of identity and agricultural way of life are intimately connected. Their conscious decision not to adopt certain modern technologies (such as fossil-fuel powered machinery) stems from their belief in the value of a simple life of physical labour. Their communities are highly self-sufficient, and throughout the farming crises of the last 40 years, the Amish have continued to live a comfortable, if simple, lifestyle. While other agricultural communities have seen many farmers forced to abandon farming and move away, Amish communities have remained strong. Because they continue to farm organically, their land remains free of many of the problems plaguing modern agriculture.[16]

Traditional agriculture clearly involves tiring physical labour. But contrary to commonly-held perceptions, such work is generally performed at a relaxed pace in a spirit of celebration. Agricultural work is in many ways a social occasion, with family members of all ages interacting with each other and with neighbours. Many of the agricultural tasks we might view as very tedious were done in a congenial social setting and in a beautiful natural environment. In Ladakh, for example, people always have time to chat or to share a cup of tea or beer, even during the harvest, the busiest time of the year. During the winter months when agricultural work is minimal, people pass their time socialising, telling stories, singing, dancing and participating in weddings and religious festivals, many of which last for weeks.

In most pre-industrial cultures, the earth was treated with great reverence and honor as the source of life. The cyclical view of reality common to most traditional cultures emphasised the renewal brought with each passing year, and the obligation of each generation to pass on lands that were as fertile as those received from their ancestors.

Local Knowledge

The dominant Western view from colonial times to today portrays traditional farmers as backward and irrational, as impediments to agricultural development. But in fact, these farmers possess intimate and detailed knowledge of their surroundings and make use of sophisticated classification systems of flora, fauna, soils, microclimates and lunar cycles. Decendants of the Mayan Indians of Central America, for example, can recognise over 900 species of plants.[17]

There have always been a few Westerners who recognised the sophistication and productivity of traditional agriculture. John Voelker challenged the colonial belief that agriculture on the Indian subcontinent was primitive and backward when he wrote in 1893:

'Nowhere would one find better instances of keeping land scrupulously clean from weeds, of ingenuity in device of water-raising appliances, of knowledge of soils and their capabilities, as well as of the exact time to sow and reap, as one would find in Indian agriculture. It is wonderful, too, how much is known of rotation, the system of "mixed crops" and of fallowing...I, at least, have never seen a more perfect picture of cultivation.'[18]

Traditional farmers engage in constant experimentation and adaptation to fit local situations. A recent international conference of practitioners concerned with the promotion of sustainable agriculture in the South concluded that farmers have shown a remarkable ability to 'classify, choose, improvise, adapt and test... The local experts are not so much researchers as farmers themselves.'[19]

Research in West Africa has shown that small farmers—not agricultural experts trained in the industrial system—are largely responsible for most of the innovations in agriculture in the region during the last decade. These farmers continue to rely on their own systems of experimentation, rather than placing their trust in 'experts', most of whom are working from theoretical models or on information provided by fertiliser or pesticide manufacturers. Farmers found agronomic experts to be of little use, unless they were familiar with local conditions and were willing to live and work in the villages.[20]

Productivity of Modern vs. Traditional Agricultural Systems

The conventional view is that modern industrial agriculture is far more productive than the traditional systems which preceded it. Yet comparisons of the productivity of the two types of agriculture are often flawed in a number of ways:

- The baseline for comparison is most often a period when agriculture had already been distorted by colonialism.
- Aggregate statistics exist for only a handful of crops such as wheat, rice or maize, and only record what was traded in national markets. Accurate data for traditional agriculture systems that produce a wide variety of crops, most of which is consumed locally, do not exist.
- The figures on grain yield increases resulting from the introduction of Green Revolution techniques fail to account for the loss in productivity of associated products, such as fuel, fodder, fibre, and fertiliser.[21]

The amount of certain grain and animal crops sold in urban centres did increase substantially between the time of decolonisation and today. But the trend in *total* production per hectare from *pre*-colonial times to the present is much less certain. For example, surveys of 800 villages around Madras, India before agriculture had been affected by colonial rule revealed average rice yields of 8.2 tonnes/ha. In the 130 villages with the most productive land. Many individual fields produced over 10 t/ha. Average yields in all villages was 3.6 t/ha. These numbers compare very favourably with current industrial yields in India of 5-6 t/ha.[22]

Recent studies of peasant agriculture in Brazil, Chile, Colombia, Ecuador and Guatemala have shown small farms to be three to fourteen times more productive per acre than large farms, which are often producing cash crops using industrial methods.[23] In one particularly striking comparison, the traditional swidden agriculture of the Kyapo Indians of the Brazilian Amazon was found to be far more productive than recently introduced systems of agriculture or livestock raising. Kyapo yields per hectare over a 5-year period are roughly 3 times that of colonist agriculture, and *175 times* that of livestock grazing.[24] The greater productivity of small farms has been confirmed by others, including the World Bank.[25]

The productivity of traditional agriculture is consistently underestimated—and industrial yields overestimated—by a system biased towards industrial agriculture. Data is also distorted for reasons varying from the avoidance of taxes to the manipulation of numbers to gain foreign aid.[26]

Dr. U Khin Win, managing director of the parastatal organisation that controls agriculture in Myanmar (Burma), recently proposed that his staff of agronomists, including 120 Western-trained PhDs, begin working at the village level in order to learn from peasant farmers. Dr. Win's innovative proposal was based on his own experience that the peasants were resourceful and extremely knowledgeable about local varieties and conditions. Previous research programmes, designed and administered from the capital, had proved ineffective in helping the rural poor. Dr. Win's proposal met with great resistance from extension workers unwilling to live in the villages. This further underlines the need for farmer-centered development.[27]

The Study of Traditional Systems

The plant breeders of the Green Revolution have for decades looked to traditional agricultural systems as sources for genetic raw materials. Yet researchers have only recently begun to pay attention to the entire traditional system. The term *agroecology* has been proposed to refer to a new scientific discipline that defines, classifies, and studies agricultural systems from an ecological and socio-economic perspective. Agroecology attempts to provide methods to diagnose the health of agricultural systems and to describe the ecological principles necessary to develop sustainable production systems.[28]

No traditional system was perfect. But by studying traditional agriculture, researchers hope to illuminate some of the principles underlying these long-lived systems, principles which can aid in the reform of modern systems and the improvement of farming in the South. (Table 10-3 lists some of the many organisations in the field). This approach contrasts sharply with conventional agricultural development, which offers a standard package of industrial inputs and techniques intended to completely replace indigenous practices.[29]

Table 10-3. Organisations Working with
Traditional Agriculture

Organisation	Location	Areas of Activity
CATIE	Costa Rica	Crop systems that mimic natural rainforest
Institute for Sustainable Agriculture Nepal	Nepal	Permaculture based on traditional hill farming
Int'l Centre of Insect Physiology and Ecology	Kenya	Pest control, intercropping
International Institute for Tropical Agriculture	Nigeria	Agriculture in Nigerian rainforests
Ladakh Project	Ladakh, India	Holistic development; information on dangers of industrial farming
MASIPAG	Phillipines	Rice species diversity, disease resistance
Neosynthesis Research Institute	Sri Lanka	Home forest gardens
PPST	Madras, India	Interaction of technology, society, culture, religion; impact of modernisation
PRATEC	Peru	Andean knowledge systems, cosmovisions
Winrock International	Thailand	Paddy culture
Networks*		
AGRECOL	International (headquarters-Switzerland)	Directories, bibliography, research
CIKARD	International (headquarters, Iowa, USA)	Clearinghouse for research on indigenous knowledge
CLADES	Latin America	NGOs improving economic and environmental viability of small farms
ILEIA	International (headquarters, Netherlands)	Research, documentation on low-external input agriculture

* see Appendix B for more information and addresses.

Techniques of Ecological Agriculture

I n the North, where the problems of industrial agriculture are most widely recognised, there is now a growing movement towards ways of farming that are more in balance with the needs of people and the land. A small group of dedicated farmers have laid the foundation for today's ecological agriculture movement.

A detailed discussion of specific practices is beyond the scope of this book because, unlike industrial agriculture, more ecologically sound agricultural models embody a range of techniques which vary widely from place to place.[1] It is, however, instructive to look at some of the common principles which lie behind ecological agriculture as it is now practised in the North. Interestingly, there are some clear parallels between the new 'post-industrial' agriculture and traditional, 'pre-industrial' agriculture.

Perhaps the most commonly accepted term for ecologically sensitive agricultural practices is 'organic'.[*] Organic farming is not merely a collection of techniques, but an entire system of management. All components of the system reinforce one another, working synergistically to maintain a healthy and productive agricultural ecosystem. Successful organic agriculture requires a detailed knowledge of local conditions and an appreciation of the strengths and weaknesses of a particular farm. Organic methods strive to work with the natural environment rather than seeking to dominate it, and attempt to harmonise with an ecosystem's complex web of inter-

---

[*] It is important to realise that this and other similar terms are often 'stretched' or misused. With the increasingly popular concern for environmental issues in general and for the way we grow our food in particular, everyone is wanting to jump on the ecology bandwagon. As a result, even biotechnology companies now go to great lengths to convince consumers that their products are 'natural', 'ecological' 'biological', and even 'organic'.

connected processes rather than expecting the system to conform to artificial norms.

Soil fertility is maintained by the use of leguminous crops, livestock manures, naturally occurring minerals, and organic wastes. Damage from insect pests, weeds and diseases is limited by diversity throughout the farm, and held in check through biological or mechanical control. Organic farmers avoid the use of synthetically-compounded fertilisers, pesticides, growth regulators and livestock feed additives.

Nurturing Soil Fertility

Organic farmers treat soil as a precious, living, renewable resource that must be nurtured and sustained. Soil health is recognised as having a direct impact on the health of the crops, animals and human beings which derive sustenance from it. The organic farmer attempts to create favourable conditions for the thousands of different species of microorganisms whose interactions make nutrients available to plants. *Rhizobia* bacteria fix nitrogen, mycorrhizae interact with plant root hairs to facilitate the uptake of nutrients, and a wide range of other organisms—including earthworms, fungi and bacteria—decompose organic matter into the simpler forms needed by plants.

Biological organisms are also important for maintaining soil structure. Soil must be properly structured if it is to retain water and air, provide anchorage for plants, and offer space for roots to grow. Earthworms, whose castings help immensely in maintaining a proper 'soil crumb structure', have been found to be much more abundant on farms managed organically than on industrial farms.

'Closing the loops'—the process of returning to the soil that which has been taken from it—is also critical to the maintenance of soil fertility. Crop residues, animal manure, human waste, and waste collected off the farm can be combined to return all of the nutrients lost through harvesting. (Unfortunately, most sewage sludge and municipal wastes are too contaminated with heavy metals from industrial processes to be useful as additives.) Decomposition processes in well-constructed compost heaps or windrows can generate temperatures high enough to kill weed seeds and pathogens, while helping to make nutrients more available to plants. Ecological farmers also replace nitrogen by planting leguminous species, which harbour nitrogen-fixing bacteria in nodules on their roots. These plants can be rotated with other crops, intercropped, or planted as an off-season cover crop that is later ploughed into the soil. A wide variety of nitrogen-fixing crops are available to farmers (Table 11-1).

Objectives of Organic Agriculture

The goals and principles of organic farming are summed up in the standards document of the International Federation of Organic Agricultural Movements (IFOAM):

- To produce food of high nutritional quality in sufficient quantity;
- To work with natural systems rather than seeking to dominate them;
- To encourage and enhance biological cycles within the farming system, involving microorganisms, soil flora and fauna, plants and animals;
- To maintain and increase the long-term fertility of soils;
- To use as far as possible renewable resources in locally organised agricultural systems;
- To work as much as possible within a closed system with regard to organic matter and nutrient elements;
- To give all livestock conditions of life that allow them to perform all aspects of their innate behaviour;
- To avoid all forms of pollution that may result from agricultural techniques;
- To maintain the genetic diversity of the agricultural system and its surroundings, including the protection of plant and wildlife habitats;
- To allow agricultural producers an adequate return and satisfaction from their work, including a safe working environment;
- To consider the wider social and ecological impact of the farming system.

Additives rich in organic matter help to aerate the soil, regulate moisture content, prevent wind and water erosion, maintain the balance of micronutrients, nurture beneficial organisms such as earthworms, and regulate pH. Composting, spreading of manures, and ploughing-in of cover crops must be carefully adapted to local climatic conditions, or nutrients—especially nitrogen—can be lost through leaching and volatilisation. Depth, direction, and timing of ploughing are also important for controlling erosion and maintaining fertility in the upper layers of the soil.

**Table 11-1. Nitrogen Fixation by
Different Crops (kg/ha)**

White clover/grass	150-200
Red Lucerne/grass	230-460
Lucerne	300-550
Field beans	150-390
Peas	105-245
Lupins	100-150

Source: Kahnt (1983) adapted by Lampkin (1990)

A Swedish field study—comparing the relative effects of chemical and organic fertilisers on soil structure and crop quality over an 18-year period—concluded that organic fertilisers have significant advantages. Applications of fertilisers were adjusted so that the total nutrients supplied in both cases were approximately equal, and thus yields did not vary significantly. Under similar tillage conditions, the organic soils exhibited much better structure, leading the researchers to conclude that 'an enlivening influence has penetrated deeper' with the organic treatment. The organically grown crops were of generally better quality, and were rated superior in terms of protein, storage life, pathogen infection, and taste. Scientists noted that the plants treated with chemical fertilisers seemed to have more difficulty regulating their growth processes.[2]

Cultivating Genetic Diversity

Over the millenia, the major food crops have adapted to a whole range of different ecosystems and microclimates around the world, giving rise to a great wealth of genetic variety. This variety is absolutely critical to the future of agriculture, since it provides the only long-term guarantee against disease and other causes for crop failure, while allowing each given piece of land to be exploited to its fullest potential.

In stark contrast with industrial practices, organic techniques contribute directly to the preservation of genetic diversity, by encouraging the cultivation of crops which are best suited to the particular characteristics of the specific farm.

While local varieties may not produce yields as high as those of hybrids (when the latter are furnished with all the necessary inputs), they have the advantage of being able to reproduce themselves. This year's harvest supplies next year's seeds, and dependence on outside markets is reduced. Moreover, researchers have shown that, using techniques of quantitative inheritance, it is possible for open-pollinated varieties to equal the yields of hybrids.[3]

The careful combination of plants in rotation or in polyculture can produce a variety of synergistic benefits. Nitrogen-fixing plants leave valuable nitrogen in the soil which is then available for subsequent plantings or for adjacent plants. Exudates from pea and vetch roots stimulate the absorption and uptake of phosphorus, nitrogen, potassium and calcium in grains. Intercropping can produce other beneficial effects: it can result in higher total production through more intensive use of a plot of land; it can modify microclimates, as when one plant shades another or provides shelter from wind and rain; it can help to prevent the spread of pests and diseases; and it can harbour beneficial animal life. Tree crops are especially valuable in multi-crop systems.

Most commercial organic farmers in the North rely more on crop rotations than intercropping. Crop rotations tend to be less labour-intensive, and are thus more appropriate in a market where labour prices are high relative to crop, energy, and machinery prices. The design of a rotation scheme that sustains fertility while being economically viable is one of the biggest challenges facing today's farmers. Among the factors farmers must consider are the following:[4]

- Crops should be suited to local climate and soil types.
- Deep rooting crops should follow shallow rooting crops, helping to keep the soil structure open and assisting drainage.
- Crops with high root biomass should alternate with those having low root biomass, since high biomass provides soil organisms with material to live on.
- Nitrogen-fixing crops should alternate with nitrogen-demanding crops.
- Catch crops, green manures and undersowing techniques should be used whenever possible to reduce nutrient leaching and erosion.
- Crops which develop slowly (and are therefore susceptible to weeds) should follow weed-suppressing crops.

- Leaf and straw crops should be alternated to aid weed suppression.
- Crops that are particularly susceptible to disease or pest outbreaks should be repeated only after time intervals sufficient to suppress the pest or disease.
- Crop mixtures should be used whenever possible.
- Autumn sown and spring sown crops should be alternated to distribute work load and supress weeds.
- Planting designs should balance labour availability, tillage requirements, and market conditions.

Weed and Pest Control

Many conventional farmers have become so dependent on herbicides that they cite the problem of weed control as the biggest obstacle to their conversion to organic farming. It is true that if an industrial farmer simply stopped using herbicides while otherwise continuing as before, weeds would be likely to overwhelm the crops. However, once an agricultural ecosystem has been restored to health through standard organic practices, weeds are usually a minor problem.

The issue of 'weeds' is an example of the differences between industrial and ecological ways of thinking. A conventional farmer views any plant other than the cultivated crop as a weed which needs to be eradicated. By contrast, an organic farmer recognises that many non-crop plants are integral parts of a healthy ecosystem, and sees their benefits as habitats for natural predators and wildlife. Ironically, repeated use of herbicides has driven many native plant species nearly to extinction, leaving the hardiest plants to thrive and create greater problems than ever before.

Even with the best organic management practices, weeds sometimes reach unacceptable levels. Organic farmers use a variety of practices to help control them, such as flaming and cultivating. Detailed knowledge of the life-cycle of the weed species and precise timing are important elements to the success of any organic weed control practice.

The ecological upsets caused by industrial agriculture have also led to severe outbreaks of insects and other pests, which in turn justify further pesticide use. This vicious cycle is completely preventable. Healthy plants growing in balanced, diverse agroecosystems are to a very great extent able to protect themselves from infestation. Moreover, simply maintaining adequate organic matter in the soil has been shown to increase resistance to pests and disease.

To the extent that more 'active' measures are required, there is a whole range of methods that do not involve the use of harmful chemicals (Table 11-2)[5]. One such method involves the mixing of plant species, either in the same field or in alternating strips or patches. Some plants produce chemicals that affect their surroundings. These so-called 'allelopathic' effects seem to offer considerable potential for pest control, although as yet they have not been well studied. Since many pests recognise a suitable crop by sight or smell, plants can be mixed to confuse pests. Even planting to affect shade and air currents can limit pest populations.

The permutations of multiple cropping for pest control are almost limitless. Some examples include:

- mustard interplanted with broccoli to control flea beetles and cabbage aphids
- marigolds interplanted with cabbage to reduce cabbage worm infestation
- garlic planted among roses to help control aphids
- asparagus mixed with tomatoes to kill *Trichodorus*, a nematode
- legumes rotated with grains to reduce the build up of fungal and nematode populations
- maize intercropped with beans to reduce infestations of leafhoppers, leaf beetle, and fall army worm.[6]

Organic farmers sometimes spray crops with naturally occurring compounds or with extracts from plants. Two well-known extracts are *rotenone*, made from the root of certain legumes, and *pyrethrum*, derived from chrysanthemums. An extract made from the seeds, leaves, or fruit of the neem tree, used for centuries by farmers in Asia and Africa, is now gaining popularity in the West as a control for herbivorous insect pests. Neem extracts have shown no toxic effects on humans or mammals, and, since a wide range of active ingredients are involved there is little chance that pests will develop resistance. Experiments with other herbal extracts and extracts from compost have also shown promising results.

Table 11-2. Elements of organic pest management

Objective	Characteristic or use
Classical biological control	Introduction of preferably host-specific, self-reproducing, density-dependent, host-seeking exotic natural enemies adapted to an exotic introduced pest, resulting in permanent control.
Augmentative or inundative biological control	Mass propagation and periodic release of exotic or native natural enemies that may multiply during the growing season but are not expected to become a permanent part of the ecosystem.
Conservative biological control	Management of the biota of the entire agroecosystem to enhance and conserve existing natural populations of native or introduced natural enemies, such as through use of polyculture, strip cropping, and organic soil amendments.
Competitive control	Use of innocuous organisms to increase competition for ecological niches occupied by pests. Such organisms may include hypovirulent strains of parasites; genetic or induced pest-resistant, highly competitive crops; sterile male insects; trap plants to divert pests from crops.
Biorational control	Use of behaviour-modifying compounds (e.g. pheromones, kairomones, repellents, attractants, anti-feedants, and food sprays) to attract parasites.
Chemical control	Use of natural compounds that interfere with metabolism, such as hormones, growth regulators, and microbial toxins.
Cultural control	Management of the agroecosystem by physical techniques such as quarantine, sanitation, rotation, tillage, cultivation, timing of operations, pruning, irrigation, fertilisation, weeding, mowing or grazing, crop isolation, scarecrows, light traps, and reduced row spacing.

Source: Batra, 1982

Mechanical means—including traps, sound, and physical barriers—have also proved effective in some cases. Scarecrows and birdscarers, of course, have been used for centuries. More recently, traps baited with pheromones, the chemical substances which act as sexual attractants to insects, have been shown to lure insects away from crops. Other relatively new methods include various machines that physically remove pests. Strawberry growers in California have developed a giant vacuum cleaner to suck pests off plants, and a machine to shake loose potato beetles was recently invented in Germany.

As a last resort, organic farmers may turn to biological control. Biological control augments the populations of natural predators through captive breeding and release. For example, large populations of the predatory chalcid wasp have been used to control whitefly. In some cases the controlling agent may be bacteria, as in the use of *Bacillus thuringiensis* against potato beetle and cabbage white butterfly.

Biological control may include the release of predators that feed on many different insects. Ladybird beetles and dragonflies are two of the better known insects in this category. Sterile insects of the same species released at crucial moments in the breeding cycle have also been used to control harmful insects. Life-cycles of pests are carefully monitored to employ control measures when pest populations are most vulnerable.[7]

Responsible Animal Husbandry

Animal husbandry is an integral part of organic farming. Most organic farmers rotate fields between leys and arable crops. Grass clover leys are the major source of fertility in the rotation, and grazing livestock on these fields allows farmers to earn a return while building fertility. Manure from animals serves as one of the main fertilisers.

The principles of organic animal husbandry are similar to the principles that apply to other aspects of organic farming. As much as possible, animal feeds are produced on the farm, and all animal waste is cycled back to the land. The health of animals is maintained by providing diet and living conditions adapted to the physiology of the animal. This implies treating animals as sentient beings rather than as unfeeling machines. Organic farmers do not use drugs prophylactically; strengthening an animal's natural immunity minimises the need for most medicines. And since animals are just one component in a diversified system, the farmer is protected in the unlikely event of a major disease outbreak.

Consider an organic dairy operation as an illustration of these principles. The basis for production is the cows' diet. Cows are rotated among pastures or enclosed strips of grassland with careful attention to total stocking densities and the life-cycles of the plants in the pasture. Fodder crops such as turnips, swedes, mangels and fodder beets provide important dietary supplements, and along with hay and silage constitute the winter diet. Cows have been found to have better appetites and to use feed more efficiently when fed organically raised fodder.

The design of housing allows cows to exhibit their normal physical and social behaviour. Stalls are designed to allow cows to stand or lie down in the same way they would in an open field. Straw bedding, good ventilation, and frequent removal of wastes are important as well. The cows are provided with the opportunity to follow their instincts to scratch, move about, play, lie down, and evolve a herd hierarchy. Calves are initially allowed to stay close to their mothers, and farmers provide attention and nurturing to newborns. The development of a personal relationship between the farmers and the cows has also proved to be important. Stress is known to depress the functioning of the immune system, and a system that allows animals to live naturally in a stress-free way leads to healthier animals.

Well-treated cows can remain healthy and productive for ten lactations or more, while cows in industrial dairy operations usually produce for only two or three lactations. A herd with an older average age allows more stable social relations to form among the animals, as well as deeper human-animal bonds. Older cows produce a better colostrum to protect their offspring against infectious diseases.[8]

If an animal should become diseased, organic farmers use a variety of herbal remedies, homeopathy, or traditional treatments and husbandry practices that have often been ignored with the introduction of new drugs. Unfortunately, these remedies are often not well known, and knowledge is being lost as older farmers leave agriculture. For example, a treatment for mastitis was developed years ago that combined herbal treatment with a balanced organic diet, including weekly supplements of seaweed and garlic. The treatment was quite successful, but the method has fallen into disuse today.[9] In emergencies, organic farmers use conventional drugs to save an animal's life, but the produce from the animal cannot then be sold as organic. Vaccines are used only if there is a clear threat to the animal's well-being.

US National Academy of Science Report on Alternative Agriculture

A recent wide-ranging study of alternative agriculture conducted by the Board on Agriculture of the National Research Council, one of the most prestigious scientific bodies in the United States, concluded that farmers who practise alternatives to high-input, industrial agriculture are operating successfully in all the different climatic regions of the US, that their yields per hectare are comparable to industrial agriculture, and that the negative environmental impacts are significantly less than that of conventional agriculture. The researchers noted that reducing the use of industrial inputs 'lowers production costs and lessens agriculture's potential for adverse environmental and health effects without necessarily decreasing—and in some cases increasing—per acre crop yields and the productivity of livestock management systems.' The report stated that 'wider adoption of proven alternative systems would result in even greater economic benefits to farmers and environmental gains to the nation.'

The study goes on to emphasise that farmers who have adopted alternative techniques have managed to maintain productive and profitable operations with relatively little support from government financial and educational programmes. Their success is all the more notable since 'alternative farming practices typically require more information, trained labour, time, and management skills per unit of production than conventional farming'. The report found that federal agricultural policies encourage environmentally destructive practices, and 'work against environmentally benign practices and the adoption of alternative agricultural systems'. Current research efforts are inadequate to support alternative agriculture. Most of the innovative practices have been developed by farmers themselves. The study concluded that, 'a systems approach is essential to the progress of alternative agriculture, and on-farm research directed towards on-farm interactions is greatly needed.'[10]

The attempt to reduce fear and stress in animals extends even to their death. Organic standards stipulate that animals be killed in the most humane way possible. Many organic farmers try to minimise transport stress by using small local abattoirs or by killing the animals on the farm.

Better Food, Healthier Environment

Food produced by organic methods is generally of higher quality than conventional produce. Organically produced vegetables have been shown to store better than conventional ones, especially under less than optimal conditions of humidity and temperature. The higher quality has been attributed to greater physiological maturity at harvest and fewer free amino acids to attract bacteria. Nutritionally, organic produce tends to be lower in dangerous nitrates and is of course largely free of pesticide residues. (The environment is so contaminated with pesticides that it is impossible to guarantee complete absence of residues.) Several studies have shown that the use of nitrogen fertilisers not only increases nitrate content, but also free amino acids, oxalates, and other undesirable componds, as well as decreasing Vitamin C. The results of one long-term comparison are shown in Table 11-3. [11]

Table 11-3. Improvement in quality of vegetables grown with composted manures compared to vegetables grown with chemical fertilisers

Desirable components	% increase (manure vs. chemical)	Undesirable components	% decrease (manure vs chemical)
Dry matter	23	Sodium	12
Protein	18	Nitrate	93
Vitamin C	28	Free amino acids	42
Total Sugar	19		
Methionine	13		
Iron	77		
Potassium	18		
Calcium	10		
Phosphorus	13		

Study conducted over 12-year period. Total yields were 24% lower when vegetables were grown with composted manures.

Source: Schuphan, 1975 in Lampkin, 1990

Perhaps the most significant advantage of organic agriculture is its effect on the environment. A recent comparison of conventional and organic agriculture drawing on research in Britain and the United

States concluded that organic farming 'enhances soil structure, extends soil cover and thus minimises erosion.' Organic farming's greater attention to efficient nutrient cycling helps maintain soil fertility, prevents pollution of water resources, and conserves non-renewable energy and mineral resources. By eliminating synthetic pesticides, organic agriculture greatly improves ecosystem health, conserves the diversity of natural flora and fauna and minimises the addition of toxic substances to the environment.[12]

Positive Trends

A s the broad implications of industrial methods of agriculture become ever clearer, people are beginning to look for more ecological, more equitable alternatives. The assumptions which supported and promoted industrial agriculture over the last decades are now being widely questioned. Around the world, farmers and consumers alike are pushing for change: away from intensive, chemical-based agricultural techniques towards more sustainable practices founded on a healthier relationship between human beings and the earth.

In the last ten years or so, the number of farmers who have rejected the use of industrial inputs has skyrocketed. Associations of organic farmers now exist in almost every industrialised country, and organic produce is widely available. The International Federation of Organic Agriculture Movements (IFOAM), which is working towards international certification standards for organic produce, now has more than 80 member organisations in 30 different countries. Membership in the California Certified Organic Farmers (CCOF), located in one of the major agricultural regions of the world, has been growing about 25% per year for the last five years, while the total number of hectares certified as organic in California more than doubled between 1988 and 1990.[1]

The amount of land farmed organically in Europe, especially in Scandinavia and Germany, has also increased significantly. In Sweden the number of hectares registered as organic has quadrupled since 1989.[2] Three thousand German farmers converted tens of thousands of hectares to organic methods between 1989 and 1990.[3] Figure 12-1 shows the extent of organic farming in Europe.

Certification as an organic farmer in most countries requires a farm to be completely free of chemicals for a number of years. For every farmer that meets these strict criteria there are many more who are reducing their use of chemicals or are already in transition to organic farming. In Britain there are more hectares in transition than the total area currently farmed organically.[4]

The Changing Attitude of Farmers

The American Farmland Trust recently surveyed a representative sample of over 1000 US farmers on their attitudes toward farming practices and the environment. They found that 'substantial support exists among farmers for changes in current farm policy that would encourage a shift to farming practices with more beneficial effects for the environment.' The majority of farmers approved of plans that would help them to cut down on the use of chemical fertilisers and pesticides. Four out of five farmers surveyed favoured changes in government price support policies that discourage crop rotation and other conservation practices. The survey respondents also emphasised the need for more research and better dissemination of information on low-input agricultural techniques.[5]

Farmers worldwide are particularly concerned about the use of synthetic pesticides; many are reducing their chemical use through biological control and integrated pest management. The US Department of Agriculture estimates that biocontrol saves farmers at least $55 million per year in avoided pesticide costs.[6] Biological control methods were recently called upon by conventional growers in the southwest United States, where a plagué of whiteflies resistant to all known pesticides has been destroying thousands of acres of fruit and vegetable monocultures. The search is now underway for natural parasitoids that prey on whitefly larvae.[7]

Cooperation has become the hallmark of the alternative agriculture movement. Farmers, consumers and researchers are forming voluntary groups to aid the promotion of organic agriculture, while certification organisations have been created to help market organic produce. Farmers have begun to support each other in informal networks, sharing information about organic techniques. In the industrialised world, there are now literally hundreds of similar organisations promoting organic farming, many of which offer internships and apprenticeship programmes.[8] Support for these organisations continues to grow. Participation in IFOAM's biannual international conferences on ecological agriculture has grown with each succeeding conference.

The Institute for Alternative Agriculture, a non-profit advocacy group in Washington DC, has seen an enormous increase in interest and membership in the last five years.[9]

Table 12-1.
Growth of organic agriculture in Europe

Country	Area Managed organically (ha) 1990	1987	% Growth (1987-1990)
	22,500	>10,000[1]	<125
Belgium	1,200	972	23
Denmark	15,500	4,000	288
Finland	11,000	<2,050[2]	>437
France	40-60,000[3]	n/a	
W. Germany	54,295	35,400	53
Hungary	3,000	0	
Ireland	3,700	1,300	185
Luxembourg	550	412	33
Netherlands	7,600	3,384	123
Norway	3,000	n/a	
Poland	1,000	0	
Portugal	550	185	197
Spain	5,500	2,700	104
Sweden	29,000	7,500	287
United Kingdom	16,000	8,619	86

Source: Lampkin, 1990

[1] 1985

[2] 1989

[3] estimates for France vary significantly because of the wide range of standards used by organisations involved in organic agriculture.

Demand for Organic Products

Farmers' concerns about the use of agricultural chemicals is echoed by consumers. Throughout the industrialised world, consumers are demanding fresher, less refined, chemical-free food. Trade in organic products has steadily expanded in the last decade. In Germany, it has grown at a rate of between 10 and 30 percent per year, while the total volume of organic produce sold doubled between 1984 and 1988.[10] Sales of organic produce in the United States is estimated to be over a billion dollars per year and growing rapidly.[11] 'Health food' and 'natural food' stores that sell organically grown vegetables and other additive-free produce are now found in every corner of Europe and North America. Organic produce has even reached mainstream supermarkets, and many food stores are starting to respond to consumer demands by giving the product's place of origin and providing information on the conditions under which it was produced.

A recent poll in Germany showed that 49% of the population would like more organic products, while other studies in the same country have consistently found that people are willing to pay 15-20% premiums for produce which has been grown without chemical inputs. Despite the presence of over 4500 specialised shops in Germany, the demand for organic food far exceeds the supply.[12] Britain faces a similar situation of high premiums and undersupply.[13]

A 1990 Harris poll found that 'for the sixth straight year most Americans believe pesticides are a more serious concern than cholesterol.' Eighty-four percent of those surveyed would prefer to eat organic fruits and vegetables, and 44% would be willing to pay higher prices. Two-thirds of the respondents agreed that there was a strong connection between organically-grown food and personal health.[14] At the same time, millions of people have reduced the amount of meat and fat in their diet, and many have become completely vegetarian.

Many people are once again raising their own vegetables at home or in neighbourhood gardens. A recent poll conducted in the United States found that 42% of all households did some gardening, with over 11 million households committed to organic methods. American gardens produce an estimated $18 billion worth of produce annually.[15]

Linking Farmers and Consumers

Direct sales between small farmers and urban dwellers have been spurred by consumer interest in fresher, chemical-free foods. Networks of organic farmers have initiated many direct-marketing projects. In the United States, the number of farmers' markets has grown dramatically in recent years. The Texas Department of Agriculture helped create almost 100 farmers' markets in 80 cities throughout the state. California has also been a leader in creating markets, featuring organic and no-pesticide fruits and vegetables.[16]

How to eat responsibly

- Participate in food production to the extent you can.
- Learn the origins of the food you buy; buy food that is produced closest to your home.
- Deal directly with a local gardener or orchardist whenever you can.
- Learn, in self-defence, as much as you can about the economy and technology of industrial food production.
- Learn what is involved in the *best* ecological farming and gardening.
- Learn as much as you can, by direct observation and experience if possible, about the life histories of the plants and animals you eat.

From Wendell Berry, "The Pleasures of Eating" in Clark, R. ed., *Our Sustainable Table*
(North Point, Berkeley 1990)

An increasing number of people are developing an even closer relationship with local farmers through schemes collectively known as 'Community Supported Agriculture', or CSA. Such schemes link individual farmers with groups of consumers, who then place regular orders for produce from the farm. The extent of interaction between producer and consumer varies from scheme to scheme. In some CSA programmes, participants actually help to work the land, and may even pre-buy 'shares' in the season's produce, thereby easing the financial burden on the farmer. All CSA schemes enable consumers to be actively involved in the way their food is grown, while giving farmers secure local markets without the need for wasteful and expensive packaging and transportation.

The close involvement of consumers in the process of growing food has the additional and extremely important effect of bringing agriculture back into the centre of people's lives. Industrialisation has so distanced us from the land that many children in the North today have almost no idea at all how the food which they eat has been produced. Direct links between farmers and consumers serve as a reminder that agriculture is ultimately the fundamental base on which we all depend.[17]

Community Supported Agriculture has existed for the last twenty-five years in parts of Switzerland, but the concept has only recently spread elsewhere. CSAs in various forms now exist throughout the continent, with the strongest interest in Northern Europe.[18] In

81

the mid 1980s the idea took root in the United States, where there are now over 200 CSAs in existence. The majority of these were started since 1990.[19]

In Japan a similar trend is underway. The consumer cooperative movement is one of the world's largest and fastest growing initiatives linking consumers and farmers. Although Japanese cooperative buying clubs have existed for over a century, their emphasis has shifted in the last twenty years towards providing higher quality, healthier food. Total membership in cooperatives rose from 5.9 million in 1979 to 9.4 million in 1985, largely because of consumers' desire for safe food. Total revenue to the cooperatives in 1985 topped $10 billion, the bulk of which came from food sales. Through grassroots initiatives by concerned housewives, the cooperatives have grown large enough to lobby effectively for consumer protection measures, to influence farmers to adopt organic methods, and to convince food marketers to reduce chemical additives and packaging. While some of the larger groups operate conventional storefront outlets, many distribute through group centres or deliver directly to households.

Safety of food, reliability, and a direct connection with growers are usually more important to members than price. The *teikei* or 'co-partnership' system has led housewives to seek out farmers directly. The Miyoshi Village Co-partnership, for example, began when a group of urban housewives travelled several hours from Tokyo to pursuade an entire village of farmers to convert to biological methods. After lengthy negotiations, they convinced the 32 farming households to provide a regular supply of vegetables, fruit, poultry, eggs and grain in a direct exchange to urban households, now numbering over a thousand. In other instances, such as the Wakabakai Society, the farmers themselves have organised to fill the cooperative's demand for biologically produced food. The cooperatives guarantee demand even for cosmetically-flawed produce, and share responsibility for decisions on what to plant and for crop failures. This has the effect of making it easier for farmers to adopt organic methods.[20]

Policy Changes

While farmers and consumers are increasingly showing their distrust of industrial agriculture, governments and public institutions around the world typically lag a long way behind. In the United States, for instance, funding for low-input research is still only one-half of one percent of the total research and extension budget. Nonetheless, there have been some clear indications in recent years that public pressure is finally beginning to have an impact even at the policy level.

One of the most important pressure groups in England is the SAFE Alliance (Sustainable Agriculture, Food and Environment Alliance), which is bringing together different interest groups—in particular, farmers, consumers and environmentalists—to campaign for the reform of agricultural policy. Their current campaign aims at restructuring government programmes so as to reward farmers for adopting environmentally-sound techniques. SAFE is also calling for legislation to eliminate the current biases in policy that favour large farms.[21]

In 1985 the European Commission committed itself to promoting more environmentally sound agricultural practices through policy reform, research, and information dissemination to farmers. In response to environmental and economic pressures, backed by growing consumer demand for organic produce, the European parliament passed a resolution favouring the promotion of organic agriculture through certification programmes, product labelling and model farms.[22]

Individual countries in the European Community have translated these intentions into action. All four Scandanavian countries and parts of Germany and Switzerland now subsidise farmers converting to organic methods. Denmark has initiated programmes to promote the sale of organic crops.[23] The Swedish parliament recently enacted an animal welfare law which requires that cattle, pigs and chickens be allowed to range outdoors, with separate areas for bedding and feeding. The new law prohibits the use of drugs and hormones except to treat disease, and requires that animals be slaughtered in as humane a manner as possible. The bill passed unopposed.[24] The European Community also banned imports of beef raised with growth hormones, due to the potential health hazards posed by drug residues.

Both Sweden and Denmark have begun programmes to cut chemical pesticide use by 50% in the next ten years.[25] The Danish government has imposed a 3% tax on pesticides to help pay for increased research, development and education on chemical-free pest control. Sweden also taxes nitrogen fertilisers to cut down on their use and to help cover the costs of fertiliser-related pollution.

The government of the Netherlands is also moving forward on environmental and agricultural reforms. Environmental standards for pesticides and nitrates have been tightened, and meeting the new standards will require a reduction in the use of chemical inputs. In 1990, a plan was adopted to reduce pesticide use 35% by 1995 and by over 50% by 2000. The government has agreed to support organic demonstration farms, and to begin research into balancing agricultural nutrient cycles, reducing pesticide use, increasing energy efficiency and eliminating nitrate contamination, by reforming fertiliser application norms and improving the handling of animal wastes. There are signs that funding will be forthcoming to meet these goals.[26] There is also movement in Britain towards tightening the regulation of pesticide residues and food additives.[27]

As of mid-1992, 110 countries had indicated a willingness to participate in Prior Informed Consent rules governing the import and export of agricultural chemicals, particularly pesticides. Under the system, information about a chemical's health and environmental risks must be made available to countries planning to import it. While the system does not guarantee that pesticides banned in countries of the North will no longer be promoted and sold in the South, it does ensure that the potential adverse effects are made known in advance.[28]

A campaign led by an international coalition of non-governmental organisations resulted in the inclusion of a chapter on sustainable agriculture in *Agenda 21*, the policy document agreed to by the 178 countries represented at the UN Conference on Environment and Development (the Earth Summit) held in Rio de Janeiro in June 1992. The document calls for "major changes and adjustments" to the industrial food production system.

In the United States there are also indications of government reform. Several years ago, the Low-Input Sustainable Agriculture (LISA) programme was started, to promote research into alternatives to conventional agriculture. Funding has increased during the last four years to a current level of $6.7 million annually. The 1990 farm bill passed by Congress authorised $40 million for the programme, but additional funds have not been appropriated. The legislation calls for retraining extension agents and for research into integrated management systems. The bill also begins to address some of the institutional barriers that actually penalise farmers for employing sound agricultural practices.[29]

The United States government has steadily tightened pesticide regulations, and hundreds of chemicals are currently awaiting retesting under the tougher laws. Certain states—including California, Iowa and Wisconsin—have enacted stricter legislation to control the spread of toxic chemicals in water. Iowa has imposed a Groundwater Protection Tax on pesticides and nitrogen fertilisers, and is using the money to fund a sustainable agriculture research programme. Minnesota, Arkansas and Wisconsin are using revenues recovered from oil companies that overcharged consumers to fund sustainable agriculture demonstration projects.[30]

Restricting The 'Dirty Dozen' Pesticides

In 1985 the Pesticide Action Network (PAN) launched the 'Dirty Dozen Campaign', seeking strict controls, bans and the ultimate elimination of twelve particularly hazardous pesticides. The original list has now grown to include 18 individual chemicals. The goals of the ongoing campaign include:

* ending the use of the Dirty Dozen pesticides wherever safe use cannot be assured;
* ensuring that human and environmental health are considered foremost in all pesticide policy decisions;
* eliminating double standards in the global pesticide trade;
* generating support for research and implementation of sustainable pest control methods.

Of these 18 hazardous agricultural chemicals, 13 have now been banned or severely restricted in most of the 70 countries charted by PAN. However, since restrictions are not always rigorously enforced, they are inconsistent in their effectiveness, and the illegal use of banned or restricted pesticides continues to occur in *all* countries. Nonetheless, the frequency of regulatory actions against these pesticides demonstrates widespread international concern about their hazards.[31]

PAN's 'Dirty Dozen' are:

Aldicarb (Temik)	Endrin
Camphecholor (Toxaphene)	EDB
Chlordane	HCH/BHC
Heptachlor	Lindane
Chlordimeform	Paraquat
DBCP	Parathion
DDT	Methyl Parathion
Aldrin	Pentachlorophenol
Dieldrin	2, 4, 5-T

Some governments have initiated programmes to protect the most degraded or sensitive land. Britain subsidises farmers in 'environmentally sensitive areas' to reduce the use of inputs that might degrade the environment. The US Conservation Reserve Program idled millions of acres of the most erodible cropland. And 1990 was declared the Year of Landcare in Australia, with the government launching a variety of initiatives aimed at reducing the country's high rates of erosion.[32]

Universities have also been pushed to respond to the demand for more research and training in sustainable agriculture. A decade ago, very few of the billions of dollars spent world-wide on agricultural research went towards sustainable agriculture, and only a very small number of researchers were involved in looking at non-industrial farming. In the last five years, however, courses in alternative agriculture have been established in many different countries, including Norway, Germany, Sweden and the Netherlands. Most of the major agricultural research universities in the US have recently established programmes dedicated to low-input agriculture.[33]

'Counter-development' and New Ways Forward

T he way we produce our food can be seen as a litmus test of industrial culture as a whole. The results of that test are quite disturbing. The modern system of agriculture continues to degrade the environment, impoverish rural communities, and force countless small farmers into bankruptcy. What is more, the status quo is not static, but is moving ever faster in the wrong direction: towards ever more artificial and potentially dangerous agricultural practices, and towards ever larger markets, which work against the interests of all but a tiny minority.

The response to these problems needs to be twofold. Most obviously, we need to explore and promote viable alternatives: ways of working the land which are socially, economically and environmentally sustainable. At the same time, and equally importantly, we need to *counter* the further industrialisation of agriculture and expose some of the myths which purport to justify it.

Counter-development

In much of the non-industrialised world, people know very little about the 'dark side' of industrial agriculture. The vested interest of governments (in both the North and South) and multinational corporations have ensured that only one side of the story is told: namely, that chemical agriculture can vastly increase yields and, therefore, wealth. Even today, the Green Revolution is portrayed as an unequivocal success. Cash-cropping is widely promoted, even among people who are not able to meet their *own* basic needs. The subsistence economy is generally dismissed as irrelevant —typically not even registering in official statistics.

Throughout the South, farmers are being led to believe that through the adoption of modern practices they can live like people in the industrialised parts of the world. There are two elements of deception here. First, no mention is made of the range of serious problems besetting the industrialised world. And second, the mathematics simply do not work: we would need four or five more *planets* if all of the world's inhabitants were to consume and pollute at the same rate as the North.

Despite the recent ecological rhetoric, the thrust of the agricultural development programmes of the major international development agencies —including the Food and Agriculture Organisation (FAO) of the UN—continues to favour the very same methods that are proving so disastrous in the North. These programmes need to be countered by putting pressure on the organisations involved to change their policies, and by providing a much fuller picture to the people in the South, thereby enabling them to make more informed choices about their own future.

In contrast with the search for practical alternatives, which would best happen in a decentralised way and at a cautious pace, this 'counter-development' can be implemented on a massive scale, and should start immediately. Across the world, an alternative information campaign is urgently needed. Such a campaign would fight the advertising onslaught of the agricultural chemical companies, draw attention to the long-term consequences of inappropriate development projects, and warn of the dangers of moving away from the subsistence economy.

The need for such a programme is by no means confined to the South. It is true that, in many industrialised countries, blatant acts of pollution and the unscrupulous marketing of dangerous products are kept somewhat more in check, both through legislation and the vigilance of pressure groups. But the citizens of the North are also being misinformed about the costs and benefits of the industrial model.

The twin driving-forces of Western culture—reductionist science and growth-at-any-cost economics—are still as powerful as ever, and increasingly destructive. The unquestioning belief in science, for instance, has led to the acceptance—with barely a whimper of protest—of the manipulation of genetic material and the creation of new life forms. Commonsense reactions against such fundamental tampering with nature are generally overwhelmed by two 'science-based' responses:

- *You can't stop progress.* (Human interventions through technology are seen as essentially inseparable from the whole process of natural evolution. In any event, 'progress' is never to be questioned).
- *Farmers have always been involved in crop and livestock breeding programmes, and the new biotechnologies are no different.* (The truth, of course, is that direct manipulation of DNA is *very* different—in scale and speed of genetic alterations—from traditional hybridisation methods.)

Meanwhile, the logic of modern economics dictates that it is good if people in Spain buy biscuits made in Scandinavia or if the apples for sale in a shop in England are grown in New Zealand. By the same rationale, citizens of the North are now generally accepting (to the extent that they are aware of them at all) the latest round of GATT negotiations and the increasing centralisation of political and economic power in Europe. Proponents of such developments make sure that the language is appealing. Who, after all can question the benefits of *free* trade or a European *community*? Public education campaigns are needed in the North, too.

Looking Ahead

The prospects for agriculture over the next century depend to a great extent on our willingness to reassess our relationship with the natural world. In particular, we need to regain respect for the diversity and complexity of natural systems, and be prepared to listen to and work with the rhythms of nature, rather than seeking to alter and control them. At the same time, we need to get beyond the obsession with short-term material profit, which has caused so much environmental, social and spiritual distress, so as to make possible a sustainable balance between real human needs and the limitations of the earth

In practical terms, this means

- Moving away from the centralising patterns of capital- and energy-intensive development towards real political and economic decentralisation

- Removing subsidies (including 'hidden' subsidies on fossil fuels) that encourage agribusiness and vast trading networks at the expense of small farmers producing for local markets
- Establishing massive campaigns to highlight the effects of large-scale infrastructural development (especially transportation infrastructures) on agriculture, on culture and ultimately on human health
- Taking steps (including the use of economic incentives) to help farmers make the transition to organic methods of cultivation
- Supporting on-farm research and regional information exchange
- Removing funding for industrial agricultural programmes in order to support the recovery of indigenous systems
- Changing the role of education (most immediately in the South, where the structures supporting a land-based economy are relatively intact) in order to restore respect for agriculture as a profession and to reflect the diversity of environments and cultures

While changes of this kind will inevitably involve disruption, both social and economic, such trouble will be as nothing compared with the massive and increasingly life-threatening breakdown which will inevitably result if we close our eyes to the crisis which we have created. In fact, we have no real alternative but to begin moving in a more ecological direction.

Leading the Way

T he development of a truly sustainable agriculture will require
fundamental changes in the way we think and act. Over the
last few decades, many individuals and groups have been
working towards radically different visions of agriculture and society.

Wendell Berry

Wendell Berry, poet, essayist and farmer, has argued forcibly and elo-
quently for decades that the crisis of agriculture is first and foremost a
crisis of culture and values. It is Berry's view that university, agribusiness and government experts are 'itinerant vandals' armed with a
fragmented abstract knowledge from which morality and responsibility are conspicuously absent. These experts have sacrificed the sus-
taining traditions of farming on the altar of industrial efficiency. Berry
proposes an agriculture based on 'intensive work, local energies, care,
and long-living communities', instead of the entertainment, exploitation and competition of industrial society, which inevitably 'depletes
both soil and people.'

Berry argues that a healthy agriculture is only possible as part of
a larger culture of nurturance. 'Volume, speed and man-hour efficiency' need to give way to 'frugality, consideration, and ecological
sensitivity.' Our survival lies in a culture in which the disciplines of
stewardship and craftsmanship are supported as natural and obvious;
where we are truly at home in a specific place on the earth. Instead of
destroying—in the name of progress—the farming cultures which
have sustained people in the past, we should cultivate and build on
their good qualities. Fundamental to the best traditions is a sense of
propriety: proper scale of farms, appropriate tools, and proper crops.
Only by approaching the diversity of the natural world with 'humility,

respect, and skill' can we ensure that the Earth, and the humanity dependent upon it, will be maintained and nourished. In Berry's vision, farming is a calling; a way of life that, when carried out skillfully and lovingly, yields a life of sufficiency and joy.[1]

Masanobu Fukuoka

A Japanese agricultural researcher who has forsaken his training in industrial agriculture, Masanobu Fukuoka has spent the last three decades seeking to develop a cultivation system that mimics nature as closely as possible. Through long years of meticulous observation and trial and error he has produced astounding results. The methods he uses on his small farm in Japan are organised around five principles: no tillage, no fertiliser, no pesticides, no weeding and no pruning. He grows rice without irrigation or transplanting. His orchards and vegetable patches resemble natural habitats. Yet through small, carefully timed interventions, he manages to produce food in quantities that equal or exceed those of industrial techniques—with none of the adverse side-effects.[2]

John Jeavons

A few decades ago Alan Chadwick synthesised the traditional practices of European and Chinese gardeners into a system he called 'biointensive gardening'. By careful preparation of seedbeds, including deep digging of the soil and careful nurturance of the biologically active upper layers, he found it possible to grow large quantities of grains and vegetables in a very small space. John Jeavons and his co-workers at Ecology Action have been trying to improve on Chadwick's synthesis for the past twenty years. Emphasising techniques to build soil fertility and paying close attention to the synergistic effects of close intercropping and crop rotations, Jeavons and his co-workers have increased vegetable yields by 400% compared with mechanised agricultural techniques. Per pound of food produced, these techniques require only one third (and sometimes much less) the water, one hundredth the energy, and a fraction of the nitrogen input of industrial farming. Jeavons asserts that in the temperate climate of Northern

California as little as 4200 square feet can provide all the food for an individual, while maintaining soil fertility without off-farm inputs. (Compare this with the current United States average of 45,000-85,000 square feet of farmland per person). Unlike industrial agriculture, soil quality gradually *improves* with the biointensive method. The work has generated widespread interest, and people all over the world are experimenting with bio-intensive techniques.[3]

Wes Jackson

Wes Jackson gave up his position as a professor in a prestigious agricultural university, and returned to his family home in central Kansas to start working towards a truly sustainable agriculture. Jackson argues that ploughing the ground and sticking in seeds is intrinsically unsustainable because it leads to the loss of topsoil at a faster rate than it is created. His suggestion is to take nature as a model. Along with a team of researchers at the Land Institute in Salina, Kansas, he is drawing on modern plant genetics to try to develop a system of perennial grasses that mimics the natural prairie eco-system, but provides the edible seeds that form the basis of the human diet. Jackson admits the research will probably take a long time, but is convinced that we must radically rethink our relation to the Earth if we are to survive.[4]

Biodynamics

Since the 1920s, a small group of farmers, first in Germany and then throughout Europe and North America, have been developing a holistic system of organic agriculture inspired by the teachings and philosophy of Rudolf Steiner (1861-1925). The biodynamic approach, as this movement came to be known, is a qualitative-ecological approach, as opposed to the analytical-quantitative approach of industrial agriculture. It attempts to combine practical experiential knowledge with insights about the interactions of spirit and matter. Biodynamic methods resemble many other organic farming systems in their adaptation to local ecosystems, self-sufficiency, integration of animals and crops, manuring of fields, etc. They differ in their close attention to the interactions between animals and plants, between wild and managed ecosystems, and between the farm and its wider environment. Close atention is paid to seasonal, lunar and other bio-chronological influences. The life processes in the soil, plants, and manure, are regulated and stimulated by the use of small quantities of preparations made from herbs and other substances. Biodynamic research and educational institutions exist in Germany, England, France, Switzerland, Netherlands, Sweden, and the United States, and associations of biodynamic farmers exist on all continents.[5]

Permaculture

The Permaculture movement is a loose network of individuals who share information and ideas on sustainable ways of living that are well adapted to a specific place. Australian Bill Mollison is credited with coining the term, and his writings provide an overview of the principles involved in permaculture design. But the movement has gone far beyond one individual or organisation, and now includes groups on every continent, while drawing on both traditional and modern techniques. Permaculturists use a detailed knowledge of a specific ecosystem to produce a rationally-designed, integrated, self-reliant system that combines water management, food production, energy supply, shelter, and wild space. They seek to make the best use of local potentials while respecting local limits. Organic agricultural techniques form the basis of permaculture systems, but they also include dedication to an outwardly simple way of life that enhances the well-being of both humans and natural ecosystems.[6]

Eco-villages

In many parts of the North—and especially in Scandinavia—groups of people are coming together to establish 'eco-villages'. This movement seeks to develop small communities that minimise human impact on the environment by meeting basic needs as locally as possible. The bulk of the village's food is produced on organically managed farms in the village or nearby. Village members take part in planning what to plant as well as actual farm work. Since food is grown close to where it is consumed, wasteful transportation, processing and storage are eliminated.

Eco-villages attempt to harmonise all aspects of life. Usually, all waste is recycled or returned to the land as fertiliser, energy is generated locally from renewable energy sources, and houses are built of local materials and adapted to the local climate. The community is designed so that people know the origin of the resources they use, and can more readily take responsibility for the consequences of their actions. Schools, childcare, and work places are all within close proximity, and community facilities and events bring people together for work, recreation, and celebration. In Sweden, where the movement is strongest, five eco-villages are in existence, twenty are under construction, and another fifty to sixty are in the planning stages. [7]

Contacts

There are thousands of groups around the world that are working for sustainable agriculture. The following list focuses on organisations that disseminate information and maintain directories of local contacts. More contacts are listed in the "Notes" at the end of the book.

AGRECOL Development Information
c/o Ökozentrum
CH-4438 Langenbruck
Switzerland
tel: (62) 601420
- sustainable agricultural development
- research
- information and directories.

Center for Indigenous Knowledge for Agriculture and Rural Development (CIKARD)
318B Curtiss Hall
Iowa State University
Ames, IA 50011
USA
tel: (515) 294-9503
- network of groups and individuals working with indigenous agricultural knowledge
- publishes *CIKARD News*
- information, directories, research index

Committee for Sustainable Agriculture
PO Box 1300
Colfax, CA 95713
USA
tel: (916) 346-2777
fax: (916) 346-6884
- US organic farming network
- sponsors annual conference
- organic produce marketing service
- analysis of agriculture-related legislation
- publishes monthly *Organic Food Matters*

El Consorcio Latino Americano Sobre Agroecologia y Desarrollo (CLADES)
Casilla 97
Correo 9
Santiago, Chile
tel/fax: (233) 8918
- network of Latin American NGOs
- research, training, information dissemination
- publishes *Agroecologia y Desarrollo*

Henry Doubleday Research Association
National Centre for Organic Gardening
Ryton-on-Dunsmore
Coventry CV8 3LG
England
tel: (024) 7630 3517
- information
- research on organic farming and gardening

Information Centre for Low External Input and Sustainable Agriculture (ILEIA)
Kastanjelaan 5
P.O.B. 64
3830 AB Leusden
Netherlands
tel: (33) 943086
fax: (33) 940791

- information and research on sustainable agriculture in North and South
- publishes *ILEIA Newsletter*

Institute for Agriculture and Trade Policy (IATP)
1313 Fifth St., SE Suite 303
Minneapolis, MN 55414
USA
tel: (612) 379-5980
fax: (612) 379-5982
- information, legislative campaigns
- trade issues, especially GATT

Institute for Alternative Agriculture
9200 Edmonston Rd. Suite 117
Greenbelt, MD 20770
USA
tel: (301) 441-8777
- policy analysis
- lobbying
- publishes *American Journal of Alternative Agriculture* and *Alternative Agriculture News*

Institute for Food and Development Policy (Food First)
145 9th St.
San Francisco, CA 94103
USA
tel. (415) 864-8555
fax. (415) 864-3909
- research, information on social costs of orthodox development
- alternative visions for sustainable development
- publishes quarterly newsletter, Action Alerts, books

International Alliance for Sustainable Agriculture
Newman Center
University of Minnesota
1701 University Ave., SE
Minneapolis, MN 55414
USA
tel: (612) 331-1099
fax: (612) 379-1527
- publishes *Planting the Future*, directory of organisations working in sustainable agriculture in the South
- publishes quarterly newsletter, *Manna*

International Federation of Organic Agriculture Movements (IFOAM)
c/o Ökozentrum Imsbach
D 6695 Tholey-Theley
Germany
tel. (6853) 5190
fax: (6853) 30110
- network of 80 organisations in 30 countries working to promote ecologically and socially sound models of food production
- publishes *IFOAM Bulletin*

Rodale Institute
Main St.
Emmaus, PA 18098
USA
tel: (215) 967-5171
- also Rodale Press, book publisher
- research and information
- publishes *Organic Gardening* and *New Farm* magazines

The Soil Association
86 Colston St.
Bristol, BS1 5BB
England
tel (0117) 929 0661
- official representative of British organic agriculture movement
- certifies organic farms
- publishes *Living Earth*

Sustainable Agriculture, Food and Environment (SAFE) Alliance
21 Tower St.
London WC2H 9NS
England
tel (020) 7240 1811
- campaigns for reform of agricultural policy

Third World Network
87 Cantonment Road
10250 Penang
Malaysia
tel: (604) 373511
fax: (604) 368106
- network of groups fighting destructive development
- information, directories
- numerous publications, including *Return to the Good Earth: Damaging Effects of Modern Agriculture and the Case for Ecological Farming*
- publishes *Third World Resurgence*

Bio-Dynamic Agriculture Organisations

There are groups in many countries practising and promoting Bio-Dynamic methods of agriculture, including:

Bio-Dynamic Agricultural Association
The Painswick Inn Project
Gloucester Street
Stroud
Glos GL5 1QG
UK
tel: (01453) 759501

Bio-Dynamic Farming and Gardening Association
PO Box 550
Kimberton, PA 19442
USA
tel: (215) 935-7797

Institut fur Biologisch-dynamische Forschung
Brandschneisse 17
D 6100 Darmstadt
Germany

Permaculture Organisations

The following organisations are part of a decentralised network of practitioners and designers seeking self-sufficient living arrangements in harmony with nature. There are also local groups throughout the world. For more information or directories of local groups, contact one of the organisations below:

The Permaculture Activist
Route 1 Box 38
Primm Springs, TN 38476
USA
tel: (615) 583-2294
fax: (615) 583-2489
• publishes quarterly, *Permaculture Activist*

Permaculture Association
BCM Permaculture Association
London WC1N 3XX
UK

tel: (07041) 390170

International Permaculture
113 Enmore Road
Enmore, New South Wales 2042
Australia
tel: (0251) 2175
* publishes *International Permaculture Journal*

Pesticide Action Network (PAN)

PAN is an international coalition of over 300 organisations in 60 countries opposing unnecessary use and misuse of pesticides, and supporting safe and sustainable alternatives. There are six regional centres:

Africa (Anglophone):
Environment Liaison Centre International
PO Box 72461
Nairobi, Kenya
tel: 2 562015
fax: 2 562175

Africa (Francophone):
Environnement et Developpement du Tiers Monde
B.P. 3370
Dakar, Senegal
tel: 224229
fax: 222695

Asia/Pacific:
PAN Asia and the Pacific
PO Box 1170
10850 Penang, Malaysia
tel: (604) 870271
fax: (604) 877445

Europe:
PAN Europe
c/o Pesticides Trust
23 Beehive Place
London, SW9 7QR
England
tel: (020) 7274 9086
fax: (020) 7274 9084

Latin America:
Red de Acción Sobre Plaguicidas America Latina
Apartado. Aéreo 1440
Palmira (Valle)
Colombia
tel: (227) 52259
fax: (227) 35252

North America:
PAN North America Regional Center
965 Mission Street, #514
San Francisco, CA 94103,
USA
tel: (415) 541-9140
fax: (415)541-9253

Notes

Chapter 2, New Seeds: Meeting Corporate Needs

1. Shiva, Vandana. *Staying Alive*. (Zed, London, 1988).
2. Doyle, J. *Altered Harvest*. (Viking, New York, 1985).
3. Korneck, D., H. Sukopp. "Rote Liste der in der Bundesrepublik Deutschland ausgestorbenen, verschollenen und gefährdeten Farn- und Blütenpflanzen und ihre Auswertung für den Biotop-und Artenschutz". (Bonn, 1988).
4. Baldock, D. *Agriculture and Habitat Loss in Europe*. (Worldwide Fund for Nature, London, 1990).
5. Royal Society for Nature Conservation and the Wildlife Trusts Partnership, *Focus on Meadows*. (RSNC, England, 1991).
6. Arden-Clarke, C. "Farming Systems Impact on Wildlife Habitat". *The Environmental Effects of Conventional and Organic/Biological Farming Systems*. (Political Ecology Research Group, 34 Cowley Rd, Oxford OX4 1HZ, 1988) Part IV.
7. "Fuglefaunaen pa konventionelle og økologiske landbrug", *Miljoprojekt*. Nr. 102. (Miljostyrelsen, 1988).
8. Doyle, J. *Altered Harvest*. (Viking, New York, 1985); Goldberg, Rebecca, Jane Rissler, Hope Shand, and Chuck Hassebrook. *Biotechnologies Bitter Harvest*. (Biotechnology Working Group, Washington D.C., 1990).

Chapter 3, Chemical Fertilisers: Artificial Abundance

1. *World Development Report*. (World Bank, Washington, D.C., 1984).
2. Arden-Clarke, C. *The Environmental Effects of Conventional and Organic/Biological Systems*. (Political Ecology Research Group, 34 Cowley Rd, Oxford OX4 1HZ, U.K., 1988), Part II Section 11; Widdowson, R. W. *Towards Holistic Agriculture: A Scientific Approach*. (Pergamon, Oxford, 1987), Chap 2, pp. 9-35.
3. "Tungmetaller i svenska jordar", *Naturmiljon i Siffror: Miljostatistisk Arsbok*. (Statistiska Centralbyran, Stockholm, 1987) p.89.
4. "Fernlehrgang Ökologie und ihre Biologischen Grundlagen", *Datensammlung*. (Universität Tübingen, 1986).

5. Papendick, R.I., Elliot, L.F., Dahlren, R.B., "Environmental Consequences of Modern Production Agriculture: How can alternative agriculture address these issues and concerns", *American Journal of Alternative Agriculture.* 1(1), 1986.
6. Snow, J., T. Mills, and M. Zidar. *Nitrates in Ground Water in Salinas Valley California.* (Flood Control and Water Conservation District, Monterey County, Salinas, California, 1988).
7. Arden-Clarke, C. "Farming Systems Impact on Wildlife Habitat". *The Environmental Effects of Conventional and Organic/Biological Farming Systems.* (Political Ecology Research Group, 34 Cowley Rd, Oxford OX4 1HZ, 1988) Part IV.
8. Unestain, T. "Modeller for mykorrhizaus betydelse i marken", [Models for the importance of mycorrhizae in the soil], *Konsubutavdelningeus Rapporter.* No. 40, University of Agriculture, Uppsala, Sweden.
9. Chaboussou, F. "La résistance de la plante vis-a-vis de ses parasite", in Besson, J.M., and Vogtmann, H., eds. *Towards a Sustainable Agriculture.* (Proceedings of the 1977 IFOAM Conference (Aarau, Wirz, 1978); Chaboussou, F. *Santé des Cultures--Une Révolution Agronomique.* (Flammarion, Paris, 1985); for a short summary in English of Chaboussou's work see: Lutzenberger, J.A., "How Agrochemicals Feed the Pests that Destroy the Crops", *The Ecologist.* 14(2), 1984.
10. Tenakoun, M. "Traditional Agriculture in Sri Lanka", *The Ecologist.* 12(5), 1982.
11. Dudley, N. *Nitrates: The Threat to Food and Water.* (Green Print, London, 1990).
12. as reported in *Harrowsmith*, November/December 1987.
13. Taylor, G. "Nitrates, Nitrosamines, and Cancer", *Nutrition and Health.* 2(1), 1983; Aubert, C.M., "Nitrates in Vegetables: Some Possible Toxic Effects", in *Nutrition and Health.* 2(2), 1983; Ferrando, R. *Traditional and Non-traditional Foods.* (Food and Agricultural Organization, Rome, 1981), FAO Serial No. 2 pp. 19-23.
14. Johnson, C.J. et al. "Fatal Outcome of Methemoglobinemia in an Infant", *JAMA, Journal of the American Medical Association.* 257(20), May 22-29, pp. 2786-7.

Chapter 4, Pesticides: The Deadly Solution

Pimentel, D. and G.A. Edwards. "Pesticides and Ecosystems", *Bioscience.* 32, 1982, pp. 595-600.
2. Coye, Molly J. "The Health Effects of Agricultural Production". Dahlberg K. ed., *New Directions for Agriculture and Agricultural Research.* (Rowan and Allanheld, Totowa, New Jersey, USA, 1986).

3. California Assembly, Office of Research of the California Legislature. *The Leaching Fields: A Non-Point Threat to Groundwater*. (Joint Publications, Sacramento, CA, 1985).

4. Kreuger, J. K., N. Brink. "Losses of Pesticides from Agriculture", *Pesticides: Food and Environmental Implications*. (International Atomic Energy Agency, Proceedings series, Vienna, 1988).

5. Dudley, N. *The Poisoned Earth: The Truth About Pesticides*. (Piatkus, London, 1987); Brink, N. "Environmental Constraints on "Agricultural Production", F.M. Brouwer, A.J. Thomas, M. J. Chadwick, eds. *Land Use Changes in Europe*. (Kluwer Academic Publishers, for Stockholm Environment Institute and IIASA, Dordrecht, Boston, London, 1991). pp. 243-247.

6. While pesticide usage increased dramatically in the United States in the 30 years prior to 1974, pre-harvest insect losses actually rose-from 7% to about 13%. Pimentel, D., et al. "Pesticides, Insects in Foods, and Cosmetic Standards". *Bioscience*. 27(3), 1977.

7. Dover, M. and B. Croft. *Getting Tough: Public Policy and the Management of Pesticide Resistance* (World Resources Institute, Washington DC, 1984).

8. Voitl, H. *Das grosse Buch vom Biologishen Land*. (Gartenbau, Wein, 1980).

9. Chaboussou, F. 1977, 1985, op. cit.

10. Weir, D., M. Shapiro. *The Circle of Poison*. (Institute for Food and Development Policy, San Francisco, 1981).

11. Lampkin, N. *Organic Farming*. (Farming Press, Ipswich, U.K. 1990), p.215.

12. ibid. p. 215.

13. Postel, S. "Controlling Toxic Chemicals". L.P. Brown et al. *State of the World 1988*. (W. W. Norton, New York, 1988).

14. The London Food Commission. *Food Adulteration and How to Beat It*. (Unwin, London, 1988).

15. Hoar, S.K. et al., "Agricultural Herbicide Use and Risk of Lymphoma and Soft-Tissue Sarcoma" in *JAMA: Journal of the American Medical Association*. 256(9), September 1986. This study was substantiated by a later study on Nebraska farmers that showed a three-fold increase in non-Hodgkin's lymphoma risk associated with exposure to 2,4-D more than 20 days a year. Zahm et al. "A case-control study of non-Hodgkin's lymphoma and agricultural factors in eastern Nebraska", (abstract) *American Journal of Epidemiology*. 128(9), 1988.

16. Maddy, K.T. "Pesticide Use in California and the United States", *Agriculture, Ecosystems and Environment*. 9, 1983, pp. 159-172.

17. "Another Man's Poison", *Amicus Journal*. (Natural Resources Defense Council, New York, Fall 1985); "What Agribusiness Does to You—The Toxic Effects of Pesticides on Humans", *Soil Association Quarterly Review*. (The Soil Association, Bristol, U.K., September 1984).

18. Schwartz, D.A., and J.P. LaGerfo, "Congenital Limb Reduction Defects in the Agricultural Setting". *American Journal of Public Health*, 78, No. 6, 1988, pp. 654-657.
19. Agarwal. A. et al. *The State of India's Environment: 1984-1985*. (Centre for Science and Environment, New Delhi, 1985).
20. *Amicus Journal*. (Natural Resources Defense Council, N.Y., Spring 1985).
21. United States General Accounting Office. "Registration and Tolerance Reassessment Remain Incomplete for Most Pesticides", Statement of Peter F. Guerrero, Associate Director of the Environmental Protection Issues, Resources, Community and Economic Development Division, before the Subcommittee on Toxic Substances, Environmental Oversight, and Research and Development at the Committee on Environment and Public Works, U.S. Senate, May 15, 1989, (GAO/T-RCED-89-40).
22. Van den Bosch, R. *The Pesticide Conspiracy*. (Prism Press, Dorchester, 1980).
23. United States General Accounting Office, 1989 op.cit.
24. Pesticide Trust. *The FAO Code: Missing Ingredients, Prior Informed Consent in the International Code of Conduct on the Distribution and Use of Pesticides*. (Pesticide Trust, London, 1989).
25. Weir, D. 1981, op. cit.
26. "The Pesticide 'Circle of Poison': Exporting Pesticides, Creating Problems", (Greenpeace Action. 1436 U St. NW, Suite 201A, Washington, DC 20009, 1991). 4 pp.

Chapter 5, Animal Husbandry: Farm as Factory

1. Pye-Smith, C., R. North. *Working the Land: A New Plan for a Healthy Agriculture*. (Temple Smith, London, 1984).
2. Dawkins, M.S. *Animal Suffering—The Science of Animal Welfare*. (Chapman and Hall, London, 1980); Robbins, J. *Diet for a New America*. (Stillpoint Press, Walpole, New Hampshire, 1987).
3. Guillot, J.F., et. al." Anti-biotherapy in veterinary medicine and antibiotic resistant bacteria in animal pathology", *Rec. Med. Vet.* 159(6), 1983, pp. 581-90.
4. Coye, M. 1986, op. cit.
5. Schell, O. *Modern Meat*. (Random House, N.Y., 1985); Robbins, J. *Diet for a New America*. (Stillpoint Press, Walpole, New Hampshire, 1987).
6. Robbins, J. *Diet for a New America*. (Stillpoint Press, Walpole, New Hampshire, 1987).
7. Robbins, J. 1987, op. cit.
8. Hefferman, William, D. "Review and Evaluation of Social Externalities", Dahlberg, K., ed. *New Directions for Agriculture and Agricultural Research*. (Rowan and Allanheld, Totowa, New Jersey, 1986).

9.   Hodges, R.D. and A.M. Scofield. "Agricologenic Disease—A review of the negative aspects of agricultural systems", *Biological Agriculture and Horticulture*. 1, pp. 269-325.
10. Tudge, C. "Variety in Vogue", *New Scientist*. 18, March 1989, pp. 50-53.
11. Sachs, C., T. Bowser. "Environmental consequences of the Structure of Agriculture: The Case of South Eastern Pennsylvania Farms," Allen, P., D. Van Dusen, eds. *Global Perspectives in Agroecology and Sustainable Agricultural Systems*, proceedings at the Sixth International Conference of the International Foundation of Organic Agriculture Movements (University of California Agroecology Program, Santa Cruz, California, 1988).
12. Moen, J.E.T., W.J.K Brugman. "Soil protection programmes and strategies in other Community member states: examples from the Netherlands", H. Barth, P. L'Hermite, eds. *Scientific Basis for Soil Protection in the European Community*. Proceedings of EC symposium, Berlin, October 1986. pp. 429 - 436. As cited in Arden-Clarke, 1988, op. cit. p. 99.

Chapter 6, Mechanisation: The Technological Treadmill

1.   *Amicus Journal*, Fall 1985.
2.   Soule, J., D. Carre, W. Jackson. "Ecological Impact of Modern Agriculture", C. Ronald Carrol, John H. Vandermeer, Peter Rosset, eds. *Agroecology*. (McGraw Hill, New York, 1990), pp. 165 - 188.
3.   Brown Lester. "Eroding the Base of Civilization", *Journal of Soil and Water Conservation*. 36(5), 1981, pp. 53-73.
4.   Soule, J.D., J.K. Piper. *Farming in Nature's Image*. (Island Press, Washington D.C., 1992). pp.14-16.
5.   Brown L. et. al. *The State of the World 1991*. (Norton, N.Y., London, 1991) p.7.
6.   Lucas, R.E., J.B. Holtman, L.J. Connor. "Soil Carbon Dynamics and Cropping Practices", William Lockeretz ed. *Agriculture and Energy*. (Academic Press, New York, 1977).
7.   Arden-Clarke, C. "Soil Structure and Erosion", *The Environmental Effects of Conventional and Organic/Biological Farming Systems*. (Political Ecology Research Group, Oxford, England, 1988), pp. 1-30.
8.   Pimentel, D., S. Pimentel. "Energy and Other Natural Resources Used by Agriculture and Society", K. Dahlberg, ed. *New Directions for Agriculture and Agricultural Research*. (Rowan and Allanheld, Totowa, New Jersey, 1986).
9.   Hubbard, H.M. "The Real Cost of Energy", *Scientific American*. April 1991.

Chapter 7, The Bigger Picture

1. Cornucopia Project. *Empty Breadbasket*. (Rodale Press, Emmaus Pa., 1981).
2. Morgan, Dan. *Merchants of Grain*. (Penguin, Viking, New York, London 1980).
3. Ahlberg, Brian. "Cargill the Invisible Giant", *Multinational Monitor*, July 1988.
4. Walter, H. "Family Farms, Safe Food, and the Environment." *Earth Island Journal*, (Earth Island Institute, San Francisco), Spring 1990.
5. Robbins, J. *Diet for a New America* (Stillpoint Press, Walpole New Hampshire, 1987).
6. Millstone, E. *Food Additives: Taking the Lid Off What We Really Eat*. (Penguin, Harmondsworth, U.K., 1986).
7. Piccioni, Richard. "Food Irradiation: Contaminating our Food", *The Ecologist*. 18(2-3), 1988.
8. United States Department of Agriculture figures quoted in Soule, J.D., J.K. Piper. *Farming in Nature's Image*. (Island Press, Washington D.C., 1992), p.4.
9. "Low-input Farming Systems: Benefits and Barriers", Report of the Environment, Energy and Natural Resources Subcommittee on Government Operations, United States House of Representatives, House Report 100-1097 (U.S. Government Printing Office, Washington, D.C., 1988).
10. MacCannell, D. "Industrial Agriculture and Rural Community Degradation", L.E. Swanson, ed. *Agriculture and Community Change in the U.S.* (Westview Press, Boulder, CO, USA, 1988); Strange, M. *Family Farming: A New Vision*. (Institute for Food and Development Policy, San Francisco, 1988).
11. Berry, W. *The Unsettling of America*. (Sierra Club, San Francisco, 1977). p. 31.
12. Whiting, B. "Effects of Urbanization on Children's Behavior", *Cultural Survival*, 10(4), 1986.
13. Strange, M. 1988, op. cit. p.179.
14. For example, while it took 165 bags of coffee to purchase a tractor in 1960, it took 400 bags in 1970. Similarly over the same period the cocoa-to-cement ratio increased fourfold. Since processing of agricultural products usually occurs in the industrialised countries, the original producers typically get only about 15% of the ultimate purchase price. George, Susan, Nigel Page. *Food for Beginners*. (London, Writers and Readers, 1983).
15. Economic development itself inevitably gives rise to an explosive growth in population. This has been true everywhere, including Europe. In Britain, for

example, the population at the start of the Industrial Revolution increased by more than seven-fold before eventually stabilising. Today in the South, industrial development is accompanied by a population explosion of similar magnitude. For further elaboration of this argument, see Goldsmith, E. "Development, Biospheric Ethics, And A New Way Forward", Goering, P. and H. Norberg-Hodge, eds. *The Future of Progress*. Second edition. (International Society for Ecology and Culture, Bristol, Berkeley, 1992). pp. 195-200.

16. Goldsmith, E. *The Future of Progress: Reflections on Environment and Development* (video). (Available from International Society for Ecology and Culture, Bristol, England, and Berkeley, California, 1992).

17. Cited in Lappe, F.M., J. Collins. *Food First: Beyond the Myth of Scarcity*. (Houghton-Mifflin, Boston, 1977)

18. Perelman, M. *Farmers for Profit in a Hungry World*. (Allanheld, Osmun, Montclair, New Jersey, 1977). Glaeser, B. *The Green Revolution Revisited: Critique and Alternatives*. (Allen and Unwin, London, Boston, 1987); Lipton, M. *New Seeds: Poor People*. (Johns Hopkins University Press, Baltimore, 1989).

19. De Kleine, Aarde. "Dutch Agriculture far from Sustainable", factsheet 12, April 1991; Goldsmith, E., Hildyard, N. eds. *The Earth Report 2, Monitoring the Battle for the Environment*. (Mitchell Beazley, London, 1990) p.80; both as cited in Clunies-Ross, T., N. Hildyard "The Politics of Industrial Agriculture", Final Draft, (*The Ecologist*, Newton, U.K., 1991).

20. Lampkin, N. *Organic Farming* (Farming Press, Ipswich, U.K., 1990). p. 587.

Chapter 8, Biotechnology and 'Free Trade'

1. "Special GATT Issue", *The Ecologist*, 20(6), Nov/Dec 1990; "Everything You Always Wanted to Know about GATT But Were Afraid to Ask", Public Citizen's Congress Watch, 215 Pennsylvania Ave SE, Washington D.C. 20003, November 1991.

2. Fowler, Cary, Eva Lach Kovics, Pat Mooney, Hope Shand. "Laws of Life: Another Development and the New Biotechnologies", *Development Dialogue*. (Dag Hammerjold Foundation, Stockholm, Sweden), No. 1-2, 1988. Strange, M. *Family Farming:A New Economic Vision*. (University of Nebraska Press, Lincoln and London; Institute for Food and Development Policy, San Francisco, 1988).

3. Hobbelink, H. *New Hope of False Promise: Biotechnology and the Third World*. (International Coalition for Development Action, Brussels, 1987), 68 pp.

4. Goldberg, Rebecca, Jane Rissler, Hope Shand, Chuck Hassebrook. *Biotechnology's Bitter Harvest: Herbicide Tolerant Crops and the Threat to*

Sustainable Agriculture. (Biotechnology Working Group, Washi...
D.C., 1990).
5. *Alternative Agriculture News* 10(1), January 1992.
6. *New Developments in Biotechnology, Field-Testing Engineered Organisms: Genetic and Ecological Issues.* (Office of Technology Assessment, Washington, D.C., May 1988).
7. Doyle, J. *Altered Harvest.* (Viking, New York, 1985).
8. For more on the implications of the new biotechnologies see: Lappe, Marc. *Broken Code: The Exploitation of DNA.* (Sierra Club, San Francisco, 1984); and Busch, M. *Plants, Power, and Profits: Social, Economic, and Ethical Consequences of the New Biotechnologies.* (Blackwell, Cambridge, Massachusetts, 1991).

Chapter 10, Learning from the Past

1. Traditional societies were not perfect, and it is not only within the industrial age that agriculture has been unsustainable. There is growing evidence that some earlier civilisations collapsed because of degradation of soils from poor agricultural practices. However, there is still much to be learned from traditional agriculture. The value of traditional systems is what they can teach us about the *principles* of healthy agriculture—not as blueprints to be copied exactly.
2. Marten, Gerald G. and Daniel M. Saltman. "The Human Ecology Perspective". C.G. Marten ed. *Traditional Agriculture in Southeast Asia: A Human Ecology Perspective.* (Westview Press, Boulder, Colorado, 1986). The differences between industrial and traditional agriculture are most striking where natural ecosystems are most different from the temperate ecosystems where industrial agriculture originated. For example, see a comparison of traditional and industrial agriculture in the Amazon: Hecht, Susanna B. "Indigenous Soil Management in the Latin American Tropics: Neglected Knowledge of Native Peoples" in Hecht, S., M. Altieri eds. *Agroecology and Small Farm Development.* (CRC Press, Boca Raton, Florida, 1990).
3. Nabhan, Gary P. *Gathering the Desert.* (University of Arizona Press, Tuscon, Arizona, 1985); and *The Desert Smells Like Rain: A Naturalist in Papago Indian Country.* (North Point Press, San Francisco, 1987).
4. Ruddle, K., G. Zhong. *Integrated Agriculture-aquaculture in South China.* (Cambridge University Press, Cambridge, 1988).
5. Wilken, G.C. *Good Farmers: Traditional Agricultural Resource Management in Mexico and Central America.* (University of California Press, London, Los Angeles, Berkeley, 1987), p.255.
6. Christanty, O., S. Abdoellah, G.G. Marten, J. Iskander. "Traditional Agroforestry in West Java: The *Pekarangan* (The Homegarden) and *Kebun-*

Talun (Annual Perrenial Rotation) Cropping Systems", in Marten, G.G., ed. *Traditional Agriculture in Southeast Asia, A Human Ecology Perspective.* (Westview, London, Boulder, 1986).

7. Everett, Yvonne F. *Principles for Sustainability: A Forest Model Applied to Forest Gardens in Sri Lanka.* (Department of Forestry, University of California, Berkeley, 1987).

8. Brush, S.B. "Farming on the Edge of the Andes", *Natural History* (5) 1977, pp. 32-41.

9. Nabahan, G. *Enduring Seeds: Native American Agriculture and Wild Plant Conservation.* (North Point, San Francisco, 1989).

10. Upawansa, G. K. "Lessons from Traditional Sri Lankan Agriculture", *Proceedings of the Southern Regional Seminar on Biological Methods of Pest Control.* (PPST Foundation, Madras, India, 1988).

11. Howard, A. *An Agricultural Testament.* (Oxford University Press, London, 1940).

12. King, Franklin H. *Farmers of Forty Centuries; or Permanent Agriculture in China.* (Rodale, Emmaus, Pennsylvania, 1973 reprint of 1911). Altieri, M.A., M.K. Anderson. "An ecological basis for the development of alternative agricultural systems for small farmers in the Third World", *American Journal of Alternative Agriculture.* 1(1) 1986, pp. 30-38.

13. Wilken, G.C., 1987, op.cit; Straughan, Baird. "The Secrets of Ancient Tiwanaku are Benefiting Today's Bolivia", *Smithsonian.* February 1991, pp. 38-49.

14. Wilken, G. op. cit., 1987, pp. 198-207.

15. Dewey, Kathryn G. "Agriculture Development, Diet and Nutrition". *Ecology of Food and Nutrition.* 8, 1979 pp. 265-273.; and Shiva, Vandana. *Staying Alive.* (Zed, London, 1988) pp. 97-178.

16. Berry, Wendell. "Seven Amish Farms", *The Gift of Good Land,* (North Point, San Francisco, 1981) pp. 249-263; Berry, W. *The Unsettling of America,* (Sierra Club, San Francisco, 1977) pp. 210-217; Kline, David. *Great Possessions: An Amish Farmer's Journal.* (North Point Press. San Francisco, 1990).

17. Toledo, Victor. personal communication, February 27, 1987, see also Toledo, V. *Ecology and Food Self-Sufficiency.* (Mexico, in Spanish).

18. Voelker, J.A. *Report on the Improvement of Indian Agriculture.* (Eyre and Spottiswode, London, 1893), p. 11, quoted in Shiva, V. op. cit. 1988, p. 106.

19. Chambers, R., A. Pacey, L. Thrupp, eds. *Farmer First: Farmer Innovation and Agricultural Research.* (Intermediate Technology Publications, London, 1989).

20. Richards, Paul. *Indigenous Agricultural Revolution: Ecology and Food Production in West Africa.* (Hutchinson Co., London, 1985).

21. Shiva, Vandana. *Staying Alive* (Zed, London, 1988); especially Chapter 5.

22. Dharampal. "The Past Can Feed the Future", *ILEIA Newsletter*. (6)1, March 1990, (Leusden, Netherlands), p.8; see also Dharampal, *Indian Science and Technology in the 18th Century*. (Impex, Delhi, India, 1971).

23. Lappe, Francis M., Joseph Collins. *Food First: Beyond the Myth of Scarcity*. (Houghton-Mifflin, Boston, 1977).

24. Hecht, S.B. "Indigenous Soil Management in the Latin American Tropics: Neglected Knowledge of Native Peoples", Altieri, M., S.B. Hecht, eds. *Agroecology and Small Farm Development*. (CRC Press, Boca Raton, Florida, 1990), pp. 151-158.

25. World Bank. *World Development Report 1980*. (Oxford University Press, London, 1980). p.42. Another study states, "The general conclusion...is that the small-farm sector makes better use of its available land than does the large-farm sector, largely through applying higher levels of labour inputs (family labour) per unit of land." Berry, R.A., W.R. Cline. *Agrarian Structure and Productivity in Developing Countries*. (Johns Hopkins University Press, Baltimore, 1979).

26. The authors' experience in Ladakh, India, is illustrative of the bias against traditional agriculture. Official figures indicate yields for wheat and barley at about 0.8 tonnes/ha. These were derived from rough estimates of grain produced (probably associated with tax records) and surveys of area under cultivation. The Agriculture Department, organised around the mission of distributing chemical fertilisers and pesticides, apparently never undertook field trials to verify the figures. Our own experiments and those of several other researchers indicated yields from traditional methods at 2.5 tonnes/ha or more, a discrepancy of over 300%.

27. Dr. U. Khin Win, personal communication, April 17, 1989.

28. Altieri, Miguel A. "Agroecology: A New Research and Development Paradigm for World Agriculture", *Agriculture, Ecosystems and Environment*. (Elsevier, Amsterdam; 27, 1989, pp 37-46). Other recent works on agroecology include: Cox, G.W., M.D. Atkins *Agricultural Ecology*. (W.H. Freeman, San Francisco, 1979); Altieri, Miguel A. ed. *Agroecology: The Scientific Basis for Alternative Agriculture*. (Westview, Boulder, 1987); Gliessman, Stephen R. *Agroecology: Researching the Ecological Basis for Sustainable Agriculture*. (Springer-Verlag, N.Y. 1990); Altieri, Miguel A., Susanna B. Hecht *Agroecology and Small Farm Development*. (CRC Press, Boca Ratan Florida, 1990); Carroll, C.R., J.H. Vandermeer, P.M. Rosset. *Agroecology*. (McGraw Hill, New York, 1990).

29. Altieri, M.A., M. K. Anderson. "An ecological basis for the development of alternative agricultural systems for small farmers in the Third World", *American Journal of Alternative Agriculture*. 1(1) 1986, pp. 30-38.

Chapter 11, Techniques of Ecological Agriculture

1. The literature on organic agriculture techniques is large and growing. An excellent summary of research on organic farming is provided by Nicolas Lampkin in *Organic Agriculture*. (Farming Press, Wharfedale Road, Ipswich IP1 4LG, U.K., tel. 04773 241122, fax. 0473 24051, 1990). This section draws heavily on this work. If no other source is given, the reader can assume that further details can be found in this volume. Permission to quote from this source is gratefully acknowledged. Of further interest are the proceedings of the international conferences of the International Federation of Organic Agriculture Movements (IFOAM). See for example: Vogtman, H., B. Fricke, eds. *The Importance of Biological Agriculture in a World of Diminishing Resources*. Proceedings of the Fifth IFOAM Conference. (Verlagsgruppe, Witzenhausen, FRG, 1987); and Allen, P., D. Van Dusen, eds. *Global Perspectives in Agroecology and Sustainable Agricultural Systems*. Proceedings of the Sixth IFOAM Conference. (University of California Agroecology Program, Santa Cruz, California, 1988); IFOAM *Agricultural Alternatives and Nutritional Self-Sufficiency*. Proceedings of the Seventh IFOAM Conference, Burkina Faso, 1989, (IFOAM, Tholey-Theley, Germany, 1990). A good summary text that draws on many older sources is: Widdowson, R.W. *Towards Holistic Agriculture: A Scientific Approach*.(Pergamon, Oxford, England, 1987). Many references on specific techniques are also included in the works on agroecology cited above.

2. Petersson, B.D., E.V. Wistinghausen. *Effects of Organic and Inorganic Fertilizers on Soils and Crops*. (English translation by William F. Brinton, Woods End Agricultural Institute, Temple Maine, 1979).

3. Jackson, Wes. *Altars of Unhewn Stone: Science and the Earth*. (North Point Press, San Francisco, 1987).

4. Lampkin, 1990, op. cit.

5. Batra, S. W. T. "Biological Control in Agroecosystems", *Science*. 215(8), 1982, pp. 134-139.

6. Widdowson, R.W., 1987, op. cit. pp 64-65; Altieri M., *Agroecology*. (Westview, Boulder, Colorado, 1987); Lampkin, N. 1990, op. cit. pp. 234-237.

7. Huffacher, C.B., P.S. Messenger. *Theory and Practice of Biological Control*. (Academic Press, N.Y., 1976).

8. Boehncke, E. "Organic Animal Husbandry—From Ethics to Practice", available from author, University of Kassel, Department of Agriculture, Applied Farm Animal Physiology Group, D-3430 Witzenhausen, Germany.

9. Turner, N. *Herdsmanship*. (Faber, London, 1954), as reported in Lampkin, 1990, op.cit. pp. 318-319.

10. National Research Council. *Alternative Agriculture*. (National Academy Press, Washington D.C., 1989), Executive Summary pp. 3-23.

11. Lampkin. 1990, op. cit. pp. 561-569; Table from Schupan, W. "Yield Maximisation Versus Biological Value", *Qual. Plant*. 24, 1975, pp. 281-310, as reported in Lampkin.
12. Arden-Clarke, C. *The Environmental Effects of Conventional and Organic/Biological Farming Systems*. (Political Ecology Research Group, 34 Cowley Rd. Oxford OX4 1HZ, U.K., 1988; Research Report RR-16, RR-17).

Chapter 12, Positive Trends

1. Committee for Sustainable Agriculture, (P.O. Box 1300, Colfax, California 95713 USA), personal communication, March 1991.
2. Inger Källander, personal communication, June 1991. For reports on the state of organic farming in Scandinavia see: Granstedt, Arthur, ed. "Proceedings of the Ecological Agriculture NJF Seminar, 166", *Alternativ Odling* 5, 1990, Uppsala, Swedish University of Agricultural Sciences.
3. Koch, L. "Bargeld, Bauren, Biotope", *Natur*. January 1991, pp. 44-48.
4. "Organic Production", (Soil Association, Bristol, England, March 1991).
5. "Agriculture and the Environment: A Study of Farmers' Practices and Perceptions". (American Farmland Trust, 1920 N Street NW, Suite 400 Washington D.C. 20036), 1990).
6. *Alternative Agriculture News*. 10(1), 1992.
7. Olkowski, W., H. E. Dietrick, "The Biological Control Industry in the U.S.", *Bio-Integral Resource Center Newsletter*, 14(1-3), January-March, 1992, (Berkeley, California).
8. "National and International Groups Working in Sustainable Agriculture", 23 pp. 1991; "Internships, Apprenticeships, Sustainable Curricula, Including on-farm Experience," and "Working Farms Programs in the U.S.", 11 pp. 1991, both publications from ATTRA (Appropriate Technology Transfer for Rural Areas, P.O. Box 3657, Fayetteville, Arkansas 72702, U.S.A.).
9. Dr. Garth Youngberg, Institute for Alternative Agriculture, personal communication, April 1991. (9200 Edmonston Rd., Suite 117, Greenbelt, Maryland 20770 USA; publishes *Alternative Agriculture News* and *American Journal of Alternative Agriculture*.)
10. "Bio-Boom: Die Deutschen wollen es besser haben", *Chancen*. November, 1988.
11. California Certified Organic Farmers, Santa Cruz, California, personal communication, January 1993.
12. "Bio-Boom: Die Deutschen wollen es besser haben", *Chancen*. November 1988, pp. 22-25; Vogtmann, H. "Organic Foods: An Analysis of Consumer Attitudes in West Germany", Allen, P., D. Van Dusen, eds. *Global Perspectives in Agroecology and Sustainable Agricultural Systems*.

Proceedings of the Sixth Annual IFOAM Conference. (University of California Agroecology Program, Santa Cruz, California, 1988).

13. Soil Association, 1991, op. cit.
14. *Alternative Agriculture News.* 8(10), October 1990.
15. Applewite, J. and J. Ambrosini. "Growing Food Close to Home", *The Cultivator.* 2(2), 1984, (University of California, Santa Cruz, Agroecology Program).
16. Hightower, Jim. "Perspectives: Sustainable Family Farming", *Issues in Science and Technology.* 6(1), Fall 1989, pp. 26-28; Vaupel, Suzanne. "Marketing Organic Produce in Certified Farmer's Markets", 12pp. (Committee for Sustainable Agriculture, and The Sustainable Agriculture Research and Education Program, University of California).
17. For more information on the possibilities of this concept see: Groh, T., S. McFadden. *Farms of Tomorrow: Community Supported Farms, Farm Supported Communities.* (Biodynamic Farming and Gardening Association Inc, Kimberton, Pennsylvania, 1990).
18. A tremendous variety of local groups and individuals are active in organising CSAs. See, for example, "Linking Farmers and Consumers", a booklet about the potential for CSAs in England. Available from International Society for Ecology and Culture, 21 Victoria Square, Clifton, Bristol BS8 4ES, England.
19. Getz, A. "Agriculture and Community Involvement: Worldwide responses to the challenge of reconciling economic, environmental, and social justice goals", Report for the International Intersessional Task Force on Sustainable Agriculture, in preparation for UNCED, 1992, available from Participatory Development Project, East-West Center, Honolulu, Hawaii, USA.
20. Jussaume, R.A. "The growing importance of food safety to Japanese consumers and its implications for United States farmers", *American Journal of Alternative Agriculture.* 6(1), 1991, pp. 29-33; information from the Seikatsu Club Consumers' Cooperative (2-26-17, Miyasaka, Setagaya-Ku, Tokyo, Japan) as cited in Clunies-Ross, T., N. Hildyard. *The Politics of Industrial Agriculture.* Final Draft (*The Ecologist*, Newton, Dorset, 1991) p. 70.
21. A campaign statement, list of alliance members and supporting documentation is available from SAFE Alliance, 21 Tower St., London WC2H 9NS, England.
22. European Commission. *Perspectives for the Common Agricultural Policy.* Document No. COM(85) 33, July 1985; Resolution PE 103.482, European Parliament, 1985.
23. Källander, Inger, personal communication, June 1991.
24. *Utne Reader* (March/April 1989).
25. Swedish goals were met in 1990. However, they were achieved at least partially by the introduction of new, more efficient, low-dosage herbicides. Fungicide and insecticide usage remained largely unchanged. The

government has announced a new goal of a further 50% reduction by 1995. Personal communication, Inger Källender, June 1991.

26. Terwan, P. *Produktiebeheersing in de landbouw: nieuwe kansen voor milieu in natur,* (Utrecht, 1990); Ministerie van VROM. *Nationaal Milieubeleidsplan.* (Den Haag, 1989, Parl. Doc. 21 137); Ministerie van VROM. *NMP-plus* (Den Haag, 1990, Parl. Doc. 21 137 20-21).

27. Sherman, Jill. "BMA suggests 'green card' pollution poison alert", *The Times.* London, October 17, 1990, p. 2; Erlichman, James. "Doctors Condemn Pesticide Rules", *The Guardian.* Manchester, October 17, 1990; Both articles report on release of a report of the British Medical Association's board of science and education, *Pesticides Chemicals and Health.* (BMA House, Tavistock Square, London WC1H 9JP).

28. *Pesticides News,* 15, March 1992, Pesticide Action Network, San Francisco, California.

29. *Global Pesticide Campaigner,* (PAN International, San Francisco), May 1992, p.12.

30. Hightower, Jim, 1990, op. cit.

31. *Alternative Agriculture News.* various issues 1990-1992.

32. Starke, L. *Signs of Hope.* Oxford University Press, Oxford, New York, 1990), p.56-57.

33. "Sustainable Agriculture: University Programs and Contacts", 11 pp, 1991 from ATTRA (Appropriate Technology for Rural Areas, P.O. Box 3657, Fayetteville, Arkansas 72702, U.S.A.); *IFOAM Bulletin.* 2, 1987.

Appendix A, Leading the Way

1. Among the many books of Wendell Berry, the following deal most explicitly with agriculture and culture: *A Continuous Harmony: Essays Cultural and Agricultural.* (Harcourt, Brace, Jovanovich, New York, 1975); *The Unsettling of America.* (Sierra Club, San Francisco, 1977); *The Gift of Good Land.* North Point, San Francisco, 1981); *Home Economics.* (North Point, San Francisco, 1987); *What Are People For?* (North Point, San Francisco, 1990).

2. Fukuoka, Masanobu. *One Straw Revolution.* (Rodale, Emmaus Pennsylvania, USA, 1978); *The Natural Way of Farming.* (Japan Publications, Tokyo, 1985); *The Road Back to Nature: Regaining the Paradise Lost.* (Japan Publications, Tokyo, N.Y., 1987).

3. Jeavons John. *How to Grow More Vegetables Than You Ever Thought Possible, On Less Land Than You Can Imagine.* (Ten Speed Press, Berkeley, CA, 1982); Various publications from Ecology Action of the Midpeninsula, 5796 Ridgewood Road, Willits CA, 95490 USA, including: "Biointensive Mini-farming", 21 pp.; "Ecology Action's Comprehensive Definition of Sustainability", 5 pp; "Biointensive Micro-farming: A

Seventeen Year Perspective", 29 pp; "Micro-farmers as a key to the revitalization of the world's agriculture and environment", 14pp.

4. Jackson, Wes. *New Roots for Agriculture*. (North Point Press, San Francisco, 1985); *Altars of Unhewn Stone: Science and the Earth*. (North Point Press, San Francisco, 1987); Eisenberg, Evan "Back to Eden", *The Atlantic Monthly*. November, 1989; The Land Institute, 2440 E. Wellwater Rd., Salina, Kansas 67401 USA.

5. Koepf, Herbert H. *The Biodynamic Farm*. (Anthroposophic Press, Hudson, N.Y., 1989). See Appendix B for organisations working on Bio-Dynamic agriculture.

6. Mollison, Bill *Permaculture: A Designers' Manual*. (Tagari, Tyalgum, Australia, 1988) and (Island Press, Washington, DC, Covelo, California, 1990); also *Permaculture One*. (Tagari, Stanley, Australia, 1981), and *Permaculture Two*. (Tagari, Stanley, Australia, 1979). See addresses for Permaculture organisations in Appendix B.

7. Fritz, Märta. "The Greening of Sweden", Goering, P., H. Norberg-Hodge, eds. *The Future of Progress*. (International Society for Ecology and Culture, Bristol, U.K., Berkeley, California, 1992), pp. 224-226; Eronn, R. "Ecological Living in Sweden: Ideas and Practical Experience". (The Swedish Institute, Stockholm); "Eco-villages and Sustainable Communities", a report for Gaia Trust by Context Institute, 1991, available from Context Institute, P.O. Box 11470, Bainbridge Island, Washington 98110 USA, tel. (206)842-0216 and Gaia Trust, Skyumvej 101, 7752 Snedsted, Denmark, tel. 97 93.66.55.

Index

120   *Index*